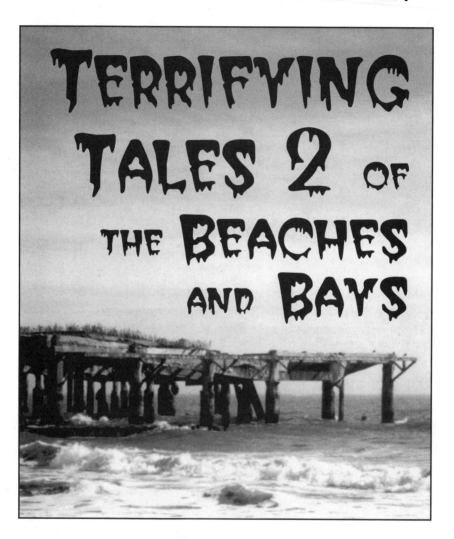

TERRIFYING TALES 2 OF THE BEACHES AND BAYS

Ed Okonowicz

Myst and Lace Publishers, Inc.   Elkton, Maryland

Terrifying Tales 2 of the Beaches and Bays
First Edition

Copyright 2001 by Edward M. Okonowicz, Jr.
All rights reserved.

ISBN 1-890690-10-4

Published by
Myst and Lace Publishers, Inc.
1386 Fair Hill Lane
Elkton, Maryland 21921

Printed in the U.S.A.
by Victor Graphics

Photography, Typography and Design
by Kathleen Okonowicz

Dedications

To my friend and mentor George Reynolds, one of the most
fascinating fellows I have ever met.
Thanks for all you've taught me.

Ed Okonowicz

To the memory of my Aunt Regina Burgoon Wineberg

Kathleen Burgoon Okonowicz

Acknowledgments

The author and illustrator appreciate
the assistance of those
who have played an important role
in this project, including

John Brennan

Barbara Burgoon

Marianna Dyal

Sue Moncure

and

Ted Stegura

for their proofreading and suggestions.

Also available from Myst and Lace Publishers, Inc.

Spirits Between the Bays Series

Volume I
Pulling Back the Curtain
(October, 1994)

Volume II
Opening the Door
(March, 1995)

Volume III
Welcome Inn
(September, 1995)

Volume IV
In the Vestibule
(August, 1996)

Volume V
Presence in the Parlor
(April, 1997)

Volume VI
Crying in the Kitchen
(April, 1998)

Volume VII
Up the Back Stairway
(April, 1999)

Volume VIII
Horror in the Hallway
(September, 1999)

Volume IX
Phantom in the Bedchamber
(June, 2000)

DelMarVa Murder Mystery Series

FIRED!
(May, 1998)

Halloween House
(May, 1999)

Stairway over the Brandywine
A Love Story
(February, 1995)

Possessed Possessions
Haunted Antiques, Furniture and Collectibles
(March, 1996)

Possessed Possessions 2
More Haunted Antiques, Furniture and Collectibles
(September, 1998)

Disappearing Delmarva
Portraits of the Peninsula People
(August, 1997)

Terrifying Tales of the Beaches and Bays
(March, 2001)

Terrifying Tales 2 of the Beaches and Bays
(April, 2002)

Ghosts
(August, 2001)

Matt Zabitka: Sports
60 Years of Headlines and Deadlines
(March, 2002)

Table of Contents

True Stories

Introduction

In the spring of 2001, we published *Terrifying Tales of the
Beaches and Bays*, which became Myst and Lace Publisher's
fastest selling book of regional stories of the unexplained.

This year, we are proud to deliver the sequel—*Terrifying
Tales 2 of the Beaches and Bays*. We've added a few more true
stories in the final section of the book and also included photographs of some of the haunted and mysterious sites in the
appropriate chapters.

Throughout history, there has been an ongoing fascination
with the sea—as a means of discovery, transportation, commerce
and recreation. But all of these historical events have generated
legends, stories and lore that oftentimes are much more entertaining and, of course, at times quite unbelievable.

Tales of ghost ships, phantom pirates, specters on the dunes,
floating lights, mysterious mermaids and visitors from another
time and dimension are commonly heard.

Whether the unfortunate craft was the *Flying Dutchman,
H.M.S. Titanic, H.M.S. DeBrack* or Uncle Charlie's *Lucky Lady*,
not so lucky ancient mariners and modern weekend boaters
have been swallowed up by the sea.

In every war, naval battles have claimed their share of crafts
and crews, and both isolated islands and popular beaches have
received the bodies of shipwreck victims.

Many believe these suffering souls still search for solace in
the soil.

In this volume, you'll enjoy true tales, based on interviews with those who have experienced unexplained events. In addition, we also include several stories of fiction, some based on local legends and lore, and others created for your enjoyment.

Thanks for reading our books and, until we meet again,

Restless Reading.

Ed Okonowicz
Spring 2002

Author's note: For complete information on all of our books, special events, storytelling programs and watercolor paintings, visit our web site at [www.mystandlace.com].

Molly on the Dunes

Indian River Inlet, Delaware

There's a ghost along the Delaware dunes and Molly McGwinn's her name. The apparition of a young, beautiful, lonely girl roaming the shoreline has been reported for hundreds of years, and while the descriptions are the same, they call her by different names—Ghost Girl, Beach Ghost, Shipwreck Sally and even Dune Demon. But most people today just refer to her as Molly–Molly on the Dunes.

It's not important that a ghost have a last name. And when she's been around for a few centuries, some would say Molly's earned the right to be addressed by her first name. That way, it makes her seem to be an actual, comfortable, matter-of-fact, accepted reality of summer beach life.

But while Molly's presence is strange, it's not unique. Sightings of other restless spirits—including pirates, Indians, lost children, Civil War soldiers, sailors and even seal people have been reported along the Delaware coast. Also, legends similar to Molly's are as old as the sea and shared in pubs and museums along ocean shores on other continents. But the story of how the ghost of Molly McGwinn came to be, and the fact that she continues to appear, is worth knowing and certainly worth sharing. So here it is.

Where to look for Molly

The phantom of a young girl in a flowing, light-colored gown appears during darkness along the dunes on the Atlantic Coast, in the vicinity of the Indian River Life Saving Station. The restored historic structure, listed on the National Register of Historic Buildings, stands along Delaware's Coastal Highway, about 3.6 miles south of Dewey Beach and about 2 miles north of the bridge spanning the Indian River Inlet.

The bright orange and deep burgundy colors of the towering, barn-like life-saving station cannot be missed, and this is reported to be one of Molly's most popular roaming areas.

The United States Life-Saving Service built the Indian River Station in 1876. It is one of six similar structures constructed along Delaware's coastline to assist shipwreck victims.

In 1915, the U.S. Revenue Cutter Service and the U.S. Life-Saving Service merged to form the modern day U.S. Coast Guard. The station and its surfmen continued to operate at the site until 1962, when a devastating storm hit the coastal area. In that year, the building was closed and the structure and grounds were transferred from the federal government to the state of Delaware.

For 86 years, the station keeper and his crew of six or seven surfmen worked year round under hazardous conditions. Each night, in fair weather and foul, they regularly walked the beaches, searching the coastline for craft that might be in trouble. During storms, the surfmen were called upon to do a bit more, namely to conduct daring sea rescues in harrowing gales, ice storms and even life-threatening hurricanes.

These rescue operations were extremely dangerous. Interpreters at the present day life-saving station museum tell visitors that, when referring to the surfmen's duty to try to save those in trouble at sea, the lifesaving service's motto was: "You have to go out, but you don't have to come back."

Life-Saving Station Museum located north of Indian River Inlet on the Delaware Coast

Along the treacherous Delaware coastline, the site of hundreds of shipwrecks and an untold number of deaths, fishermen and locals first reported sightings of Molly's restless spirit.

But it was surfmen from the life-saving station that verified the lovely ghost's presence as early as the 1890s.

The history

Two 18th-century shipwrecks–the *Three Brothers* in 1775 and the *Faithful Steward* in 1785–occurred a short distance south of the Indian River Life-Saving Station and just north of the Indian River Inlet. A state of Delaware historical marker along Coastal Highway indicates the vicinity of the crash of the *Faithful Steward* and the death of nearly 200 passengers and crew.

There are stories of a cargo of British gold in the hold of the *Three Brothers*, and barrels of Irish halfpennies are said to be a main part of the cargo of the ill-fated *Faithful Steward.* There must be some credibility to these claims, since the First State coastline near the disasters was littered with coinage immediately after the tragedies, and even today the wreck site area is referred to as "Coin Beach."

Locals say that term was "coined" in the 1930s, during the Depression, when workers from a nearby Civilian Conservation Corps (CCC) camp would collect buckets of copper coins in the Indian River area.

In the case of both of these shipping wrecks, there were hundreds of deaths and many of the corpses were washed ashore. But misfortune of this type was an accepted possibility for anyone traveling the ocean in those days. And members of families living in communities near the sea eventually became accustomed to such tragedies and weren't easily shocked by the effects of the shipwrecks.

Visit any state with a shoreline, including the coastal towns bordering the Great Lakes, and you'll hear whispered tales of old name, "respectable" families that made their fortune with the help of the weather and at the expense of the victims of tragedies at sea.

When ships crashed upon rocks, damaged cargo and dead passengers were delivered onto the beaches. Often, during the height of the storm—and, to be sure, within a short time after its end—bands of locals would swoop down from the dunes and race each other to claim the pickings.

These sea scavengers would strip the clothes off dead bodies, pull jewels from bloated fingers and pry gold from the teeth of the recently departed. They reasoned that it was their right to put their loot to good use, for the coin and clothing and precious stones were of no use to the dead, nor was the cargo–of building materials, spices, food, livestock or furniture–of any use to the unlucky ship captain.

With regularity, when the weather and sea created a storm that delivered an unexpected prize to the shoreline, the body pickers were ready to go to work and claim all they could carry off. However, when the recovery business hit a slow spell because of an uncooperative Mother Nature, enterprising rogues enacted a plan that would keep them in business and keep the valuables flowing. And that is the rest of our story.

Origin of the legend

One version of our legend describes Molly McGwinn as either an indentured servant or a distant relative of a scavenger family that resided in the marshland near the present site of Ocean View in the early 1800s. However, the extended family, which was more like a gang of thieves, had hideouts and hovels where they gathered in the Dewey Beach and Bethany Beach areas.

Harwell was the recognized elder and uncontested leader of the pack of scalawags. He had several brothers, more than one wife and scores of children, nephews, nieces and cousins—but not everyone was quite sure which kid fell into which particular category.

Molly McGwinn, who is believed to have come from Ireland, was 17 years old. It's not certain how she ended up with Harwell's mob, but it's fairly certain that she worked in his residences, doing cleaning and cooking, tending the farm animals and occasionally watching several of the master's small children.

While not classified as a "picker"—a member of the looting gang that extracted valuable items from the dead—Molly was assigned a very important task. During slow times in the scavenger business, she stood at the top of the tallest dune, not far from the treacherous rocks near the Indian River Inlet, and signaled ships, indicating that it was safe to approach the shore.

Meanwhile, Harwell–and the men, women and older children of his band–waited behind the shoreline, resting low in the tall grass, until the wooden ship smashed into the rock pile and the crew, passengers and cargo reached the beach.

With screams and howls of greedy anticipation, Harwell's ragged mob would descend upon the beach and relieve the dead—and oftentimes the not so dead—of their valuables. One large robber named Big Ben would drag a two-wheeled cart onto the beach, stake out an area as his own, and go to work. Speed and volume were Big Ben's specialties. With a short axe, he would go from corpse to corpse, chopping off limbs that he thought might host a valuable.

He used the "off with her head" approach to secure an attractive necklace—no time to fumble with the latch or break a perfectly good chain.

Then it was "away with the hand," in order to claim a splendid ring or bracelet—no time to yank the ringlet off a bloated digit.

Another rule was "take him away," when a complete set of fine clothes could be secured from a wealthy passenger's body.

One of the most horrifying sights after one of Harwell's conquests was watching Big Ben direct his cart, overflowing with body parts, away from the shore and toward the mainland. Later, beside a campfire, he would use a sharp knife to do the detail work needed to separate the deceased's valuables from the larger part of the torso or limb.

During the first few months of working for

A portion of the Delaware Dunes where Molly is said to roam

Harwell, Molly, discovered that the family business was questionable at best. Horrified, she had tried to escape more than once, but a combination of starving and beatings convinced her that she was better off doing what she was told. Besides, there was no place to go. For fear of serious retribution, no one in the area would dare consider giving refuge to someone owned by Harwell.

Molly decided to do her work and pray for a miracle. And one day it arrived.

The meeting

Nathan, the son of an English merchant, had been sent to the colonies to learn the latest business practices to improve the family's trade with America. While traveling along the Atlantic Coast, the 20-year-old, attractive Englishman spent a large amount of his time in Lewes, a major shipping port.

One afternoon, while she was leaving a small food store carrying supplies, Molly crashed into Nathan, who apologized for his inattentiveness and helped the young woman carry her purchases to her wagon.

That chance meeting turned into more accidental encounters—that had been carefully arranged by Nathan. After a span of six months and more than a dozen conversations that increased in length and substance along the streets of Lewes, Nathan and Molly were able to meet alone late one spring afternoon on the Delaware dunes.

Their mutual attraction was obvious, and he asked her if he could visit her home and ask permission of her family to call on a more regular basis.

Shocked, Molly replied, "No. I mean, it would be pleasant to see you more often, but my family is a bit unusual. Very strict. It would not be good for you to meet with them, not yet."

After explaining that he was scheduled to travel back to England within a week, Nathan asked Molly to wait for his return. At that time, he said he would go directly to her father and ask for her hand in marriage.

Afraid that any explanation of her bizarre situation would be too involved and most certainly ruin her chance to be rescued from Harwell and his gang, Molly agreed to wait for Nathan's return.

Embracing, he said, "Within six months, I will be back in Lewes and we shall be married soon thereafter." Then he produced a golden necklace from his vest pocket. Raising his arms over Molly's head, he placed the unusual engagement gift around her neck.

Looking down, Molly stared at the strange amulet dangling from the golden chain. As she took the strange shaped piece of metal in her hands and raised it closer to her eyes, Nathan pulled a matching amulet from beneath his shirt.

Taking the two charms in his hands, he placed them side by side—Molly's and his. They were halves of the same gold coin that had been cut in two.

"When I return," Nathan said, "my portion will be joined with yours. Until then, each day and night you will rest next to my heart, and I will be beside yours."

Hugging her fiancé, Molly promised to wait for him, and they arranged to meet in Lewes in six months.

"Sooner if I can arrange it," the boy said, smiling.

"Hopefully, sooner," Molly said.

Horror on the shore

That summer and early fall were the most difficult Molly had ever experienced. Knowing her lover-to-be would return before the end of the year, she counted the time in months, weeks, days, even hours. But she knew no matter what method she used the length of his absence could not be reduced.

Whenever she could skip away from Harwell's compound, Molly stood at the top of the dunes, near the inlet. It was the highest spot along the coast, and she knew Nathan's ship would have to pass that point as it entered the Delaware Bay and headed toward port in Lewes to the north.

Sometimes, she pretended that he was on a passing vessel, that she would see him sooner than expected, that he would come and take her away from the hellish life that she lived. But her wishes went unanswered.

It had been a mild summer, too few storms for Harwell's satisfaction. Six times during those months, Molly was sent to the high dune to wave her lantern at passing ships. On four occasions, her signal worked, luring unsuspecting ships into the inlets shoals.

When that occurred, Big Ben would load up his cart, Harwell's band would swoop down on the shoreline and the dead, and sometimes the living, would be separated from heirlooms and coinage, personal possessions and clothing.

Molly remembered walking away from the beach and seeing the white surf landing atop naked bodies and pulling them back from the shore. It was as if the tips of the crashing waves were trying to drag the dead back into the safety of the sea.

When September ended, Molly began to anticipate Nathan's October arrival. But when All Hallows Eve passed with no word of his presence in Lewes, she began to become depressed. Wild thoughts filled her desperate, fragile mind: What if he decided to stay in England? Perhaps he had found a wealthy London bride. Could he be in Philadelphia, partying with the elite businessmen and political leaders? Maybe he changed his mind, or forgot about me.

Then her strong sense of hope, the only thing she had left, convinced her to wait a bit longer, to persist, to have faith in her lover.

Molly decided to wait another month—before she killed herself, for that was her only means of escape. But she knew if her suicide didn't work, Harwell would make her life more miserable than it had ever been.

She first considered stabbing, but that might not work, and shooting wasn't foolproof. The weapons were unreliable and often misfired. She selected drowning. It was the easiest and most dependable way to die. Walking out into the ocean until the water was over her head, and then letting the tides do the rest, was her choice. If Nathan didn't return by Thanksgiving, she would escape Harwell and start a new life, in another eternal world where she might be better off.

It was early evening, mid November, when Harwell directed his robbers to make haste toward the coast. A merchant ship was expected to enter the bay in a few hours. Molly didn't have to be told what to do. She automatically grabbed her signal lamp and headed for the dunes.

The wind blowing off the ocean was cold, the spray biting and stinging her skin. She thought how a body would die after only a few minutes in water that cold. No need to drown. It would be easy.

If Nathan isn't here in another 10 days, she thought, I'll just walk into the ocean and be gone before the water reaches my face. Plus, she thought, as she waved the lamp back and forth on the high dune, no one will miss me. I wonder how long it will it take them to notice I'm gone—a few hours, a day, perhaps two, maybe a week at the most.

Harwell and his mob cheered as the ship changed course and headed for the shore. Molly kept waving the light. Her arms were getting tired. But that didn't matter to Harwell. If she stopped, he would have her flogged. He had done that before. Six lashes. She could tell he enjoyed that, watching the blood run down her back. But it didn't matter; soon her miserable life would change for the better.

If Nathan came back, she would be happy with him.

If he didn't return, as he had promised, she would become one with the sea—forever. Once she got cold, she thought, as the glow of her lamp passed in front of her white gown, she wouldn't be able move her arms and legs. Therefore, her decision to drown in the sea could not be altered, even if she changed her mind at the last moment.

But that's good, Molly thought. I might get scared. My resolve might weaken. So if I can't move my arms or legs, I won't be able to fight for my life, swim to shore, save myself— which I won't want to do.

That's good. That's fine.

I'm ready. Ready for . . . .

At that moment, three dozen scavengers cheered as the ship's bottom hit rock and the groaning sound of the strained and broken timbers rolled across the dark beaches.

"SHE'S DOWN!!!" shouted Harwell, jumping up and waving his arms, directing his pack of thieves toward the shore and the booty the waves were sure to deposit.

An hour later, as she sat on the high dune, she could see Big Ben loading his cart. Harwell and his wives were arguing as they claimed their share of the loot.

Near the rocks, The Merchant, as one fellow was called, tossed lamps, a sea chest and water soaked boxes into this small cart. The Merchant never took anything off a body. "I've got principles," he said quite often.

After three hours, the main work was done.

Harwell's band retreated from the scene, leaving about two dozen dead face down at the surf line. Ship debris would wash up for days, but that was left to the locals. Harwell had gotten the good stuff. "Besides," he often said, "we leave the locals a little bit to plunder to keep them happy. After all, they got to deal with what's left of the bodies, too." He would always follow that announcement with a hearty laugh, and the rest of the band would join in—except for Big Ben, who would be off alone, hacking off limbs to get to his prizes.

On this night, near the fire, as the crew was proudly sharing its finds, one of the lesser respected scavengers tossed a trinket to his woman, who was seated on the far side of the circle.

"Take this piece, my Sweet!" the squeaky-voiced thief shouted as the prize sailed through the air.

Looking at the jewel, the woman squealed back, "What's this, broken goods? I don't want no half-arsed trinket. I's worth a whole or nothin' ya damn, no good cheaper!" And she threw the piece back at her man.

Upset at being scolded in front of his male crewmates, the man hopped up, raced over and pulled his screaming wife by her hair. "Ya no good wretch! Ya'll take the half-a-gold piece and thank me for it, ya will, or I'll put out your eye with me knife, I swear!"

As laughter swelled, Molly's mind caught the tail end of the argument. The words " . . . the half-a-gold piece and thank me for . . ." gradually jarred a memory in her mind. Getting up in a slow-motion-like trance, she raced toward the fire, knocked over the man and woman, and grabbed the gold chain with the half coin, fell to the ground and screamed.

It was Nathan's necklace.

In a world that was continuing outside her sobs, and stable beyond her swirling mind, she stood up, clutching her fiancé's amulet and walked away from the fire, beyond the gathering of Harwell's world. Slowly, through the darkness, moving by instinct, she headed for the sea.

It was dawn when she reached the site of the wreck. Standing on the high dune, she looked down at the locals, good people who were leaning over bodies searching for some slight sign of life.

Laughing, she stumbled toward the line of corpses that had been moved away from the lapping waves.

"Fools," she mumbled. "You'll find none alive. Not one will be living. Harwell and his like see to that." Sobbing, she fell to her knees and began crawling, pulling the blankets off the top of each corpse.

Woman.

Child.

Old man.

Another old man.

Bearded sailor.

Baby girl wearing pink.

Young man in a vest.

Woman with a blue blouse.

Grandmother with no teeth.

Young man. . . . with . . . .

Screaming, she fell on top of the cold, wet body.

Instinctively, she stretched her arms around Nathan. Her Nathan. Her love.

Her future, which she had lured with her fire lantern to his death.

Horrified, she suddenly pulled back. Looked down on his face and saw the scowl of hate, fear of death.

It was no longer the smooth, kind look that she had seen the last time they embraced. No, it was the face of a man, a victim of evil—a kind being who had been snuffed out by his love, Molly, a common, wicked criminal, a murderer of innocents.

There would be no understanding, no forgiveness. She did not have the right to touch his body, to even look upon the dead baby, the drowned mother, the frozen cold sailor.

She moved her head from side to side. The townspeople knew. They were whispering, pointing. They may not have known that she had waved the lamp, but they knew she was involved, was one of the wrongful ones, an evil one, a she devil in human form.

Screaming, she turned and ran toward the surf.

No one tried to stop her.

They let her go, let her run to the bottomless sea where she belonged, where she would roam forever, where there would be no forgiveness for her part in the deed.

The truth

During the summer and fall, we present "Coast Ghosts" programs at the Indian River Life-Saving Station. Visitors learn about
the history of the Life-Saving Service from trained interpreters
and historians. My job is to offer ghost tales and legends of the
area. At the end of the night, visitors walk away with a good
sense of the building's history and a healthy dose of Delmarva
folklore.

The combination of history and haunts has worked well at
other historic sites where I have worked in Delaware, Maryland,
Pennsylvania and New Jersey.

I had heard of Molly's story and had been using it for years,
but I never realized how real it was, nor did I know that the
"Lamp Lady" had a real name.

In past programs, I had referred to her as the "Lady with the
Lamp." When we were preparing the first program at Indian
River's station, Barney, one of the fellows associated with the
Life-Saving Station said, "You mean you're going to tell the story
of Molly McGwinn?"

"Who's she?" I asked, surprised.

"Why, that's our Molly. Molly on the Dunes!" Barney replied,
like everyone knew about the station's resident phantom.

During the following half hour, Barney told me his version
of the Lamp Lady's story and how she has been spotted since
the late 1800s, roaming the ocean shoreline east of where the
orange and burgundy building now stands.

Verification of Molly's existence came about when surfmen
saw her at night. But, Barney said, they were afraid to write any
of the sightings down in the official station log, for fear of being
accused of drinking on the job.

Barney explained that each life-saving station was built five
miles away from the next. Each night, a surfman assigned to the
Indian River station would walk two-an-a-half miles north, where
the fellow on duty would meet a surfman from the Rehoboth
station walking two-and-a-half miles south.

They would exchange metal tags, called "Patrol Checks,"
with numbers and information on them from their respective sta-
tions that proved they were completing their duties. They sell
reproductions of these tags at the Life-Saving Station Museum
Gift Shop.

On several occasions, surfmen would see a light going straight out into the water. At other times, it looked like it was coming up out of the water and heading for shore. Some reports said it looked like a woman in a white dress carrying a lantern that would stay lit, even when it went under water.

If this was never written down, I wondered how Barney found out about Molly.

Years ago, he said, people—mainly widows and children—still living in the area that had been related to former surfmen, told the story. When the life-saving station historians heard bits and segments from several sources, they pieced the complete story together.

"Molly's still out there," Barney said. "Sometimes, when I'm up in the top floor, looking out to sea, I admit I hope to get a glimpse of her."

Have you seen her yet?, I wondered.

"Not yet," he said, smiling, "but I'm in no rush. She's been around here for more than a hundred years. She's not going anywhere."

Author's note: The Indian River Life-Saving Station Museum and Historic Site is open daily, 10 a.m.-5 p.m., Memorial Day to Labor Day. The site offers living history, volunteer programs and a gift store with a wide array of nautical and regional items. Special program, including the "Coast Ghosts" presentations—where other unusual events in the old building are discussed—are scheduled annually. Call for details about special programs, directions and the off-season operating schedule, at (302) 227-0478.

Haunted House
on the Ocean

Atlantic Coast, U.S.A.

Some cops like to talk and others don't. The thing about cops that makes them more interesting than Joe Sixpack is that they have unusual experiences to share. It comes with the job. Their stories range from the fascinating to the bizarre.

The tricky thing is hooking up with a talkative officer of the law. Unless you've got a cop relative or next door neighbor, or someone you went to high school with became a policeman, getting information usually requires a referral from a mutual and trusted third party--someone who can connect the man with a badge with a tale to tell and a writer who is willing to listen.

One benefit from dealing with ghosters (the term I use to classify people associated with and interested in the paranormal) is that they frequently come looking for you. They're excited to share what they've experienced or stories they've heard so ghost writers like myself can get the tales into print.

Robert (who, I must add, refuses to respond to "Bob," and who becomes annoyed when people address him using the informal version of his name) is a reliable beach ghoster whom I've cultivated over the years. He's very satisfied to accept my bribes of free books, short visits when I'm in his seashore area and my promises to get his stories "out there," as long as I decide they are good enough to use—which they tend to be.

Soon after *Terrifying Tales* was released last spring (2001), Robert, a bit of an eccentric driftwood artist and man about town (I can't share which town or his usefulness as a story source will be detrimentally affected) called me quite early one morning.

Before I could respond to the ring of my phone with a simple "Hello," he snapped, "I can't believe you put out that book without consulting me!"

It was obvious my source was annoyed.

"Robert?" I tried to respond as I rubbed my eye while using my other hand to block out the rising sun.

Ignoring my request to confirm his identity, the ghoster went on without pausing for a breath. "After all the stories I have so graciously provided for your use in the last five years, after all of our confidential encounters, I am appalled that you have shut me out!"

"I don't understand," I replied.

He ignored me and kept going full ahead. "Enough that you hold my leads for YEARS without following up on the principals involved, after I gave them my solemn word that you would . . . ."

"Rober . . . ." There was no stopping him.

"I've let it pass when, on several occasions, I've been embarrassed to discover from my neighbors that you've slighted me and not stopped to visit while you were delivering your works to the store only a block away from my apartment . . . ."

"Look, Robert . . . ." There was nothing to do but wait until he ran out of gas.

"But this is the definitive affront, the ultimate umbrage. You have printed a book on beach horror, and, I discover, to my chagrin, that my best tale, the one from Officer Fleiss, is not included. Can you possibly comprehend what this had done to my credibility? How can I face him? How will I be able to walk the streets, the boardwalk? What do I say to him, to his family? How could you do this to ME?"

To a degree Robert had a right to be miffed.

As a result of his introduction to Detective Phil Fleiss, Robert had been responsible for the delivery of a wonderful ghostly tale that occurred at a beach town. But, as the guy told Joseph and Mary when they arrived in Bethlehem on the donkey, "There's no room in the inn!" Well, the same goes for pages available in a book. I had to hold Fleiss' story until *Terrifying Tales 2* was ready to go.

The other thing Robert and readers have to understand is: ghostwriters get several hundred leads each year. There is no way that each incident is worth writing about, and the ones that are would fill more than the one or two ghost books that each of us are able to produce. So, as a writer, you have to sort and sift and save and decide what stories go in, which are placed on hold and what leads and tales will never get any ink.

Sure, I should have alerted Robert, so he and Phil would not be shocked when the book was released. But I made a mistake. I'm human. It happens. That's what I tried to explain to Robert.

After enduring a long pause from his end of the phone line, where I pictured Robert seated near a window looking out at the Atlantic, I was granted an opportunity to speak.

Following three apologies, an excuse about forgetfulness and the final explanation that "The story was so good, I wanted to save it for the sequel, so I would be sure to have a great chapter for the readers," there was no response. I thought he had hung up.

"Robert? Are you there?"

"Yes!" came the curt response, "and that is unsatisfactory."

"What?" I said, controlling, for the time being, my aggravation. I wasn't eager to lose a good ghoster, but the last time I had been verbally abused like this was from Sister Superior in St. Hedwig's Grade School, and that was a long time ago. "Look," I added, still talking calmly, "I said, 'I'm sorry.' The story is scheduled for *Terrifying 2* and I'll send you each 10 free copies. How's that?"

"No. That just won't do."

"Well, what the hell do you want from me, BOB?"

After a pause, he said, "Now let's not act immature, Ed. I certainly don't want to be more disappointed in you than I already am." Then he added in a mocking voice, "As if that's even possible."

Before I could explode, he turned the tables on me and said, in a tone that was good natured and gave the impression that nothing untoward had occurred, "Here's my plan for your redemption into my good graces. Twenty free copies of both *Terrifying 1* and *2*, for me. Only 10 for Phil will be fine. He really doesn't care. Also, in *Terrifying 2*, I want my story to be positioned first, as the premier chapter, so booklovers will be able to enjoy it immediately. Also, I want a printed apology, to Robert and Phil, for not being featured in the original book as we had expected. No compromise. Those are my demands!"

I could have argued. I could have slammed down the phone. But what good would that have done? To a degree Robert was right, so I agreed to nearly everything he wanted. We compromised on the placement issue, and he seemed satisfied with his story being featured "very close to the front."

This is the story based on Robert's referral and Phil's experience. I hope you enjoy it,

~~~~~~

The particular haunted house on the ocean in our story faces the Atlantic. Every day of the year, when the sun inches over the horizon of the sea, the first rays connect with the pointed tips of the railing around the home's bright white widow's walk. In short order, the sunlight grows and illuminates the entirety of the gray and white, private, three-story beachfront dwelling

Because the building's owners don't want people to know their structure is haunted, and since the police officer who shared his story and official reports demanded that the actual site remain confidential, I can't indicate the town where these incidents occurred. But since my ocean-related interviews are limited to the east coast of Delmarva and the southern half of the Jersey Shore, it's safe to assume that these events took place within those geographical confines.

This Haunted House on the Ocean could be standing in Cape May, Ocean City, Stone Harbor, Lewes, Avalon, Beach Haven, Chincoteague, Rehoboth Beach, Dewey, or maybe even in the town where you're vacationing right now.

It could be across the street, down the lane, the next block over or, if fate worked its wicked wand on you, it could be the house that you're renting right now.

Read on, and see if any of the details in the following story seem familiar to you.

Detective Phil

Phil Fleiss was in his mid 50s. Beefy and red faced, he talked with a raspy growl. The cop's hefty frame, held up by a pair of fat elbows, rested in a forward hunch across the table in the far corner of a deserted beach bar. It was slow, empty, the way you would expect a seashore gin mill to be just a week before Thanksgiving.

The bartender was bored, with no college cuties to drool over and very few tips to pocket. It bothered him, but it was fine for Phil and me. We could talk freely, without interruption.

"Nothing much to do here in the freakin' winter," Phil snarled. "Deader than a two-month-old corpse."

"You ever run across one of them?" I asked, smiling, trying to encourage him to talk.

"Hell, yeah! Seen a least a dozen. You spend 20 years workin' in Philly, you seen it all." Then he paused, added, "Well, almost all," and took a sip of beer from his glass.

I waited for more. Sometimes the best way to interview is to keep quiet, avoid asking a long series of prepared questions. If the subject is a talker, he'll fill in the gaps, be eager to.

Luckily for me, Phil Fleiss was a talker.

"I tell ya," he said, shifting his eyes from side to side, as if he was afraid of being overheard. "I seen it all, mixed it up with the scum of society. Perverts. Murderers, both husbands and wives, lots of them. Even had a few teenage killers. Got a baby killer case one year. Two bastards tossed their own kid in a trashcan. Whatdya think they got for that one?"

"Life?"

Phil almost choked on his drink. Wiping his mouth, he shook his head and replied in a hiss, "Less than three years. Twenty-four freakin' MONTHS is all. And both of the little rich-kid executioners got time off for good behavior. Hell! You can get more today for smoking in a restaurant or driving home after you pop two brewskies at the club. What a messed up world."

As Phil shook his head and downed a healthy swallow, I picked up my pencil and began taking notes. He was on a roll and didn't notice.

"I worked robberies where they cut fingers off the victims to get a fake stone. Worth next to nothing. Stupid bastards. Found a body once stuffed in a fold-up sofa in an apartment. Down on South Broad. Killer left town, kept payin' the rent and the dead body was sittin' there, crammed up and bloated. Was there for weeks. Damn, seen it all in 22 years before I retired and came down here. I thought, this was gonna be a day at the beach, hell—make that a life at the beach. Check out the young chicks in bikinis. Write a few parking tickets, roust a few college drunks. That's what they told me I'd come across most.

"You ever notice that when you go to work at a new place they make it sound like you hit the 'ideal job of all jobs' jackpot? That it's the best place, got the best bennies, nicest coworkers. Hell. If that was true why the hell was there an opening in the first place. But, that's another issue. Major world issue that we aren't gonna solve here."

I laughed and nodded that I knew where Phil was coming from. He shifted in his chair and got back to his job and the story I had come to hear.

"Worst I thought I'd end up with down here in surf land was maybe a rape or petty theft. Hell," he said, shoving a manila folder across, "This one caught me by surprise. A real beauty."

On a white tab at the top edge was the case number—"0117-1998."

I opened the file and stared at the top photograph. It was a rectangular glossy of a three-story beach residence. The pad had to be worth more than a million dollars, probably closer to two mill, since it was right on the shore—unobstructed view. It was relatively new construction, and located in one of those gated compounds—with names like "Refuge" or "Preserve" and "Retreat." The kinds you drive by that have huge signs stating obvious messages, like: "PRIVATE," "RESIDENTS ONLY" and "NO BEACH ACCESS."

That means no beach access to 99 percent of the tourists and locals—basically, people who don't make in the six figures and beyond. In addition to the owners, that 1 percent includes those working stiffs who get the okay to cross the gatehouse borderline to make a repair or delivery. Of course, you could get lucky and buy one of these properties if you hit the Powerball or found Blackbeard's treasure while building a sand castle. But that doesn't happen in real life.

Neither, some people think, do ghosts.

That's what Phil thought. He admitted it.

"I was a nonbeliever," he said, then lowering his eyes toward his soggy beer coaster, as if he had just committed a venial sin.

"I was one of those guys who looked at anyone who talked about ghosts, like our mutual friend Robert, as a wack job, a loonball. Now, don't get me wrong. I'll kick back, to relax, mainly, and watch movies and videos about poltergeists, Halloween crap—the cable channels got those specials on all the time. I see them at two in the morning when I can't sleep.

"But that's just entertainment. Fun stuff. Something to fill the time. No way was it real. No way, Jose. I see the wackos they interview on those programs and I would never, ever, put myself in that league.

"Even after a few voodoo, chicken-killing cases in the North Philly projects, I never gave this stuff any thought. Just a bunch of crazies howlin' at the moon. As long as they left everybody else alone, let them go off and do their thing. That was my approach."

"What happened?" I asked, spreading about 10 photos of the exterior and interior of the haunted beach house in front of me on the saloon table.

"We got a call," Phil said. "Nothing special, I thought. Woman said there were noises in the basement. Cryin', moaning sounds, something banging around down there. Now, you gotta understand, in this job, in every damn job, it's location, location, location. Ya follow me?"

"You're saying the call came from a rich neighborhood and it had to be treated appropriately."

"Bingo!" Phil said, snapping his index finger in my direction like he was aiming the barrel of a gun.

"No matter where you go, city, country, small town, big town, and especially in any beach town, my friend, remember this: Money talks. We get a call from Front and Grunt, hell, they can wait. No big rush. Even if there's a stabbin' or fight. If it's not high profile, you don't kill yourself to get there. If you're lucky, they'll knock each other out by the time you arrive. So go safe and smooth on the ride over. Unless it's a brother or sister on the force in trouble, of course."

"Of course," I replied, agreeing with him and urging him to keep talking.

"But, you get the ringle from Highbrow Lane, I don't care if it's a kitty cat in a tree, you better move your ass over there pronto. And be sure to tell them it was a pleasure getting little

Poofy or ChaCha or Fluffy back into the rich owner's waiting arms. Because . . . . ," he paused.

Without pause I picked up his sentence, " . . . .they make the big bucks, pay the most taxes and will be on the phone to their personal friend, the mayor, two minutes after you leave their front door—especially if you didn't bow low enough or if you tracked in dirt on their imported rug."

"You ever been a cop?" Phil asked, laughing and saluting me with his nearly empty glass.

"Nope," I said, "just worked for a lot of people who knew they were important, and I learned how to play the game."

"Right. So we go over there, post haste."

At the house

Phil said that when they arrived, after midnight, the lady of the house was waiting at the front door. She was well dressed, wearing jewelry that should have been locked in a safety deposit box and, of course, hysterical.

Phil's partner, Jeff, a young kid only two years out of college, followed behind the owner into a foyer that looked like an entry hall of a cathedral.

"I'm talkin' Homes of the Rich and Famous, here," Phil said, shaking his head. "She's pacin' back and forth, back and forth across this fancy inlaid tile and the kid is standing quietly with me. But his eyes are bulgin' outta his sockets, lookin' straight up at the ceiling in this three-story foyer—like it goes up to heaven. He's never seen something like this. I gotta elbow him in the ribs to bring him back down to Earth to take notes while we're getting' the basics from Mrs. Richie Rich."

As Phil paused to take a sip of a refill, I showed him an interior shot, which gave a view of the foyer he had just described. He nodded, then explained the photographer took the shots the next day, at Phil's request.

"I needed him to go back there and take pictures in the areas that me and the kid went through the night before."

"Why?"

"To help me convince myself that I didn't see what I knew I saw."

I shook my head, indicating confusion. Phil grabbed the

folder, pulled out a few other shots taken in the basement, which showed a finished off game room and a door leading into the rough area that held all the mechanical systems—including heater, sump pump and storage.

"That's where all the shit happened," Phil said, "right there!" He stabbed the tip of his finger into the picture, indicating a corner behind the heating unit.

As he began to give me the meat of the story, Phil explained that the official report does not contain what happened, only photographs, a statement that the detectives investigated the complaint and no intruder was found and nothing out of the ordinary was apparent.

"If I put down what I saw, even if I included a picture of me swearing on a stack of *Holy Bibles*, I'd be the laughing stock of the station. Hell, they'd probably have me out there at high noon, in the bakin' sun, checking expired meters on a bike wearin' one of them goofy helmets and short pants that make cops look like circus clowns. So I kept quite, and the kid—because I told him his career would be in the toilet if he spoke up—he clammed up tight, too."

I asked what happened to his partner.

"Quit, just a few months later. Selling stocks and financial shit, now. No hassle. Regular hours. People say 'Thank you very much.' No rolling over drunks and holdin' up college kids while they're barfin' on the sidewalk or boards. Anyway, we get there and Mrs. Nob Hill tells us her husband's out of town, and she's all alone and scared to death and she said she thinks there's someone in the game room in the lower level."

After Phil gathered basic information about the resident and her concerns, he said he told her to stay in her first-floor study, with the door locked, while he and Jeff checked things out.

A set of wide stairs, that were accessible through a door in the kitchen, led to the lower level, which was like a half-basement surrounded by built up sand, with a door that opened out onto the beach. The moment Jeff and Phil opened the door, an oppressive rotten egg stench passed over them in a thick wave. The smell only lasted in the air a few seconds, but it was heavy enough that its nauseating effects lingered as they reached the bottom of the wooden stairs.

Pausing, Phil hit the light switch, which, of course, didn't work. Taking a small flashlight from his jacket pocket, he directed the thin beam around the large recreation room. The light passed over a wet bar, lounge furniture, antique beer mugs and old-fashioned liquor advertisements that were hanging from the ceiling and on the walls.

Phil stopped the beam's movement when it illuminated the door at the far end of the room—the entry into the storage and mechanical area.

There were no sounds or banging as the owner had described. Slowly, Phil grasped the antique, glass knob and, before he turned it and pushed open the door, the older detective turned back to see if Jeff was ready. The younger man, with a pistol in his right hand and flashlight in his left, nodded.

Swiftly, Phil shoved open the door and dove forward, crouching as close to the floor as possible. Jeff waited behind, his back pressed against the wall just beside the open door frame.

"When I hit the floor, another wave of stink hit me like a brick," Phil said. "This one was worse than the first, and it didn't go away. Stayed right there. I wanted to gag. Grabbed my tie and pressed the bottom up against my mouth and nose and tried to crawl forward. I yelled back to the kid, Jeff, told him to get in there with me. I knew when he hit the doorway, because he started to cough. I couldn't warn him. When he caught up to me, we were both on our knees. Reminded me of rotting flesh."

Leaning back in the booth, Phil paused, lit up a smoke and said. "This ain't nothin' yet. The good part's comin'. I mean, if I was all alone, I'da been outta there. Long gone. But I got this kid, and he's scared as me, I can tell. So I figure I better keep it together to keep him from chuckin' his cookies or losin' his composure. I turn and give him a forced smile, like I done this a few dozen times, and he nods back, but he knows I'm lyin'. Then we start to get up, and at the same time each of us is tossing searchlight beams from floor to ceiling lookin' for an intruder or a bloated stiff or who the hell knows what."

The two men didn't split up, but stayed side by side, walking slowly around the unfinished section of the basement, when Jeff hit the older man's arm.

"The kid slams me with his elbow, and I just about shot him, I was wound up so tight. I didn't want to find anything. The stench was less by now, maybe bearable. I was ready to be headin' for home. No intruder found. Negative results. Tell Mrs. Rockefeller to get her sewer flushed and don't call me again. Thanks for the interesting evening. Call a plumber or a honey dipper to clean out her septic next time.

"But Jeff was stiff. His elbow pressed against my side. He shuts off his light and points to the far corner of the cellar. All the way across the foundation."

Phil reached across the table, pulled another photo from the file and shoved it at me with his finger pressed over the section where two foundation walls met.

Floating figures

"Right there. As God in heaven is my witness, me, and the kid, too, we see this baby. This tiny baby, and it's floatin' in mid air. It's bare ass naked, totally uncovered, but so small. Like it's just born. But there's blood all over the poor little thing's chest and legs and face. Now I'm thinkin' I am ready to sign the papers, commit myself, 'cause there's no way this is happenin'. But I toss a quick glance at Jeff and he's blanche white. His skin is the color of white foam on the top of a fresh cold one. I swear to God. And he's not movin', just lookin' straight ahead, like somebody chiseled him there.

"When I turn back to look over at the corner, there's a woman, wrapped in a white sheet, with bloodstains all over the bright sheet. She's moanin' and screechin' like a banshee. It sounded like a howl, like the voice of death comin' through the woods or across a frozen pond. Death. It was death for sure. Shit, I was so scared, and while we're goin' through all this crap, the temperature must have dropped 50 degrees. I mean, I could see my breath makin' clouds in front of my face."

Phil said he and Jeff didn't move, they couldn't. He said the room became so cold that he imagined they were locked in a meat freezer.

"All we could do was watch, watch this screamin' ghost or whatever, chase this dead baby back and forth across the cellar. After about the third time the creatures passed in front of my line of sight, it flashed through my mind that they were like the bear at the boardwalk shootin' gallery—back and forth, back and forth. Left to right, over and over. And I wondered if the sequence would ever stop."

Eventually, the figures floated back into the wall, Phil said. Immediately after they disappeared, the police officers were able to move their fingers and limbs, and begin to regain control of themselves.

After enduring the stench and the heat and then the sudden shift to icy blasts of cold, plus the sighting of the two apparitions and discussing what they saw, Phil figured they were downstairs at least 20 minutes, maybe more.

"When the ghosts or whatever were gone, they took the moaning and the smell with them," Phil said. "I had no trouble convincing Jeff to keep his mouth shut when we got upstairs. We would work out a rational explanation in the car on the way back to the station."

But, when they got upstairs and asked the owner to come out of her study, she became upset.

"She says 'NO!' Screamed that she wasn't comin' out until we went downstairs and checked around."

Phil said he tried to explain that he and Jeff had been through the entire basement and had found nothing. But the owner shouted that they could not have done anything in less than three minutes. She demanded that they return downstairs.

"Now I'm thinkin' she's on the sauce, and I knew I was soon gonna be. The kid, who's so close to me that I can feel his breath on my neck, is whisperin' there is no way he's goin' back down into the freakin' bowels of hell. No way at all. Plus, I know I'm not going down there again ever, not alone, not with him and not with an army. So I yell to Mrs. Gotrocks that we'll be pleased to go down again, and that she should stay in her room until we return. Then I checked my watch and directed Jeff to follow me into the kitchen."

Jeff and Phil sat on the kitchen floor for about 15 minutes, nervously trying to kill time. They discussed football, women, lifeguards, sex, drugs and gambling–anything but what they thought they had seen on the floor below.

"No way in hell was I gonna mention what went on down there at that time, not in that nuthouse. The words might have conjured up some spirit to come through the floor. What we saw could wait until we were in a more stable place. Besides," Phil said, "that gave us more time to try to forget it ever happened."

"Did it really?" I asked the cop.

"Hell, yes!" Phil snapped back. "I have not one iota of doubt that we saw something horrifying in that hell hole. Now, there were lots of moments of doubt and confusion about what it was or might have been. But there were several strange incidents from that evening that didn't add up."

The time discrepancy was a major source of confusion, Phil said. There was no way only a few minutes could have passed when they were in the basement. It had to be almost seven to even 10 times that. The owner said she smelled nothing unusual before, during or after the police arrived. She also swears that the two detectives were only away a few moments the first time.

"When we returned to see the lady of the house the second time, we got outta there fast. Convinced her she had been hearing things, but we added that it would be good, in order to get a good night's sleep, that she consider staying that night with a nearby friend until morning. We also said we would send a photographer to her place the next day, to take some 'routine' shots.

"She took our advice and asked us to drive her to a neighbor's home and we did. Then we went back to the station."

Phil said he never returned to the haunted house, but other cops had gotten calls over the years—both before and after his visit. But no one had ever experienced what he and Jeff had seen.

"The strange thing," Phil said, "is that we went in there in late June. Soon afterwards, I found out that the owners moved out and left the place vacant the rest of the season. Now, they had a fancy house in Georgetown, D.C., but to leave a prime property like that unused all summer was strange."

The next year, they rented the property, and the following year it was sold. Phil said keeping track of the Haunted House on the Ocean became a personal hobby of his. He noted that it changed ownership three times in the next six years. But each time he approached the owners, through a phone call, to get a few comments about the home and their decision to sell, he met resistance.

" 'No comment' would sum it all up," Phil said. "Strange, and not just to me. Real estate people started whispering that the place was jinxed. Now, they didn't really mind, since they got commission every time the place changed hands, but the price remained at a mill and a half, not cheap, but not up there like the other beachfronts could get. Now it's only a rental. Owners never use it, and the occupancy is sporadic. I talked to a girl in one of the rental offices and she told me, on the quiet, that they have a rough time keeping it occupied and most people who sign a lease don't complete the one or two weeks they pay for."

The amalgamation of strange circumstances and curious facts, plus his detective instincts that demanded a solution to every problem, sent Phil on his own treasure hunt. He said he wanted to find out what might be the cause of the strange visions that he and Jeff saw that summer night in June so many years before.

"And?"

"And what?" Phil replied, then added a smile that indicated he wanted to string me out a bit longer.

I waited in silence, playing his game.

He was so proud that he couldn't hold back and eagerly told me how he had solved the puzzle, at least to his satisfaction.

"Since I couldn't find anything out from the local officials," Phil said, explaining that indirect inquiries of the mayor and a few old timers had turned up no pay dirt, he said, "I decided to check the property records. Went to the county courthouse. Hell, other than contractors and lawyers, nobody normal visits those people and asked normal questions. So I went in, acting totally ignorant and placed myself at their mercy. I was treated like a king. For a few cold sodas and a pie and cake, they went back and typed me up a list of property owners of the buildings and land. Went back a few hundred years. And, bingo, I got what I needed. In fact, I got more than I ever expected."

The county deed records indicated that the land upon which the haunted house now stands, Phil said, was the site of a home for unwed mothers up until the 1940s. Wealthy families from Boston, New York City and Baltimore and Washington, D.C., would pay dearly and send their daughters--who had "gotten themselves into trouble," or "into a family way"–to give birth to their unwanted children at the "Seashore Home," as it was called for many years.

"Of course," Phil said, "the family would tell everyone that little Ruthie had gone to stay with old ill Aunt Emma for a few months, to help out with a family emergency. Then, a half year later, the young girl would return to school and society without the burden of the unwanted child, who had been placed up for adoption with a "nice family" somewhere far, far away. And life returned to normal for everyone—usually."

"So that's it?" I asked. "It was a home where they delivered babies and some of them died. So the ghosts are the women and children that died there?"

Phil smiled, stood up and said he needed to hit the men's room, but he suggested that I wait for his return and, "the rest of the story."

To save time, I ordered him a fresh cold one. As beer flowed, so too did conversation. I didn't want anything to interfere with the final chapter of Phil's beach horror.

My subject returned with the strut of a conqueror. Lifting his glass, Phil toasted me, added his thanks for my patience, and said, "I could have let things go at that. Most people would. But I pushed it further, knew there was more I could discover. Then I did some calculations. If a kid was born there in the '30s or '40s, there might be one or two of the babies born there still around. Or maybe some old timer could tell me what they had heard.

"It wasn't easy," Phil said. "It was as if every older person I spoke to denied to know anything at first. Then, one person gave me a sliver of info, and I used that to get a few more to tell me a little bit more. Eventually, I was able to pry open the crack. Then I got it all. Got more than I expected or wanted. But it helped me make sense of what happened to me that night in June."

Kate's story

Phil said he discovered that the doctor, who had delivered children at the home, had acquired a serious drinking problem. Eventually, several mothers and their newborn babies died during botched deliveries.

"A year after I began my investigation, I met this wonderful old lady named Kate," Phil said. "Lives on a family farm 40 miles from here. I won't tell you where. Don't ask how I found her. I got friends in the records office who have access to archive documents. When I visited Kate, she was delightful. Turns out she was born in the house, was one of the unwanted children, she even worked there for a while. She told me they shipped her off to a farm when she was about 13, where she lived her whole life since. She would have never known her real mother, except that one day she was visited by a wealthy woman who came by to drop off a hatbox with about 10 grand in twenties and fifties.

Kate recalled that the woman, who said she had been asked to deliver the package, was probably her mother, who was trying to clear her conscience. In her 20s at the time, Kate said she took the money. Afterwards, she was able to work less and started doing historical research on her childhood home. From a bureau drawer, she pulled out a scrapbook with pictures of the old Seashore House and a few yellowed newspaper articles about the place when it was being torn down."

Phil said he told Kate about what he and Jeff had seen in the house that currently stands on the old property.

"For a moment, only a flash in time," Phil said, "the old lady was taken aback. Walking across the room, she stood by the farmhouse window, looked outside and spoke, but she didn't look at me. She sighed, then announced that she was going to tell me something she had never told anyone else before. I got a chill. The temperature in the room seemed to drop noticably. I know this sounds crazy, but it was like she had been waiting for someone to come, for someone to ask her about the events that had happened there 60 years ago.

"She said that when she was about 10 the nurses started making her work there. Since she hadn't been adopted yet, she would assist in the operating room. Nothing complicated, just carry containers of clean water and fresh sheets. Then, she said, in a tone that was painful, like a confession, 'I could tell when he was drinking, and if there was a baby coming, it was going to be dangerous, very bad. We couldn't tell anyone. What could we do? If the townspeople found out what was happening, they would close us down. Then where would we go? What would I do? Where would I live?

" 'The nurses and I kept quiet. As long as it was only the babies that died, it was okay. But if a rich girl didn't survive it would be very bad, because they were supposed to return home. We only lost two, two young mothers that is, while I worked in the basement operating room. That wasn't too bad. But, oh, dear. Oh, my dear. There were so many little ones that perished. Twenty, maybe even close to 30 in one year. But it wasn't my fault. I couldn't do anything about them. I was only 10 or 11 then. All I could do was take them out in the back, in the high sand dune, like they told me, and bury them as deep as I could dig with the shovel. I had to go out alone in the middle of the night. If it was a full moon, we would have to keep them a few days, or weeks—downstairs in the crypt. Then, when it was black and dark, I would take them out, but only when there was no moonlight. We couldn't dare get caught.'

"She turned then," Phil said, "and she walked back to the sofa and sat across from me. Then Kate continued, her eyes offering a glimpse of the pain that was aching in her soul, 'But I was so young. What did I know? The first baby I buried, a tiny girl I could hold in one hand. She had no name, poor little one. I thought she should have a name, so I made a wooden marker and scrawled 'Amy' on a weathered board, and I shoved it in the sand, right above where I had placed her body that was wrapped in a bloody white cloth. I thought it would be nice to pay respects.

" 'The next morning, the doctor and nurse saw my wooden grave marker sticking out of the dune. They went crazy, ran out and threw it away. I got the worst beating. You see. No one knew what was going on. Just me and the doctor and the nurse. The other orphans that they had not been able to place, they didn't know anything. Only me. Only me. They said it would scare the others, if they knew we were burying baby bodies in the sand around the building.' "

Phil stopped for a moment. Grabbed hold of his beer glass with both hands, spun it a few times. When he looked up, our eyes met.

"I swear, that must have been something. That kid, out there at night, gravediggin' in the sand, all alone. Jesus! What a screwed up world! Hell. The more I learn, it's always been screwed up, not just now. Bastards. It's a wonder Kate isn't in a nuthouse."

Under the dunes

"Some story," I said. "Damn."

"Damn is right," Phil said. "The thing is, she said that she buried them in the back of the house, side, under the porch. Everywhere. And imagine when they kept them down in the crypt for a week or so until the moon went in. How the hell did that kid sleep at night?"

"So the restless souls of the dead babies and butchered mothers are roaming the foundation of a $2 million dollar beachfront that nobody seems to stay in for more than a few nights?"

"Bingo!" replied the talkative cop.

"So what are you going to do about it?" I asked.

"Not a damn thing," Phil said. "If I tell anyone but you, they'll think I'm nuts. Nobody is going to want to investigate the grounds around the property and look for baby bones from more than half a century ago. Plus, what can anyone do about it? The house is there. The moanin' ghosts are there. Let them all just be. Nothing anyone can do. Just write it up. Besides, think of all the fun this will generate."

I didn't understand immediately.

Phil explained, "How many times have you driven past those gated compounds and wondered how many of the owners had screwed their stockholders, shafted their relatives or got their money through kickbacks, payoffs, golden parachutes and loophole crap that only the rich and the politicians can get away with? Come on, you have, haven't you?"

I nodded. "Sure. I'll never live in a mansion on the water, and like most people, I'm jealous of a lot of the ones who do have property there."

"Right! So, do you or I really care if they got a few dead baby bodies floating through their foundations, or if their old ladies are hearin' moanin' and groanin' and the rattlin' of chains in the night? The answer is: 'No!'

"But the best part is, if you write this up and anybody reads it, every time one of these corporate big shots that owns a $2-mill beach house hears a creak or groan, or sees a flash in the night, they might think their place is the one right on top of the Seashore Baby Burial Slumber Spot. And just the fact that they might not get a good night's sleep, because they can never be sure if their place is haunted, is satisfaction enough for me."

Author's note: To my friends "Bob" and "Phil." Please accept my apology for not including this story in the first book of *Terrifying Tales*, as we had discussed.

Olden Place Along Graveyard Gut

Southern New Jersey

New Jersey is flat, especially the southern end of the state that is crisscrossed by water in the form of meandering creeks, unnamed guts, winding streams and quicksand-like bogs. Anyone familiar with marshland would swear the area looks exactly like its sister territories located in nearby Delaware, Maryland and Virginia.

In each of these Mid-Atlantic states are scores of sleepy villages steadily approaching ghost town status. While they're not there yet, you can tell the ones that are headed in that direction. Most are located off the main drags, along part of a network of back roads that only the locals really navigate with confidence.

Their main streets see little traffic and are lined with a growing number of vacant storefronts sporting faded "For Rent" signs desperately calling out for attention. The old wooden churches are in need of a paint job, and a handful of neglected and overgrown cemeteries offer a strong clue that their aging congregations have sacrificed perpetual care of the dead in favor of more pressing heat and electric bills that address the immediate needs of the living.

Going through a water town, you'll surely see rows of weatherworn boats. Perched in rotted dry docks over untended, weed-covered lots, these relics of better days on the river are in desperate need of repair. You can almost hear their pleas in the wind, seeking a Good Samaritan to purchase their freedom and launch them back into the sea where they belong.

In the distance, there's the sound of lapping waves, rhythmically attacking rotted piers standing like uneven, charred matchsticks just off the shore. One wonders how many years, or maybe even months, the town has left to live before the ever-patient briars, brambles and bushes reclaim what is rightfully theirs.

These thoughts passed through my mind in the midst of a chilly fall afternoon as I sat alone at a wooden table in Wichtown's "Old-Time General Store," waiting for Darryl Nebs. On the phone the night before, my contact had promised to serve as my private tour guide to the "Olden Place," a burial site that he claimed he "had sole knowledge of and access to."

The Wichtown local added that he had a crazy story to tell. I had gone there to listen, and I sensed during our conversation that both of us were looking forward to the meeting. I needed a good tale to share with my readers and Darryl admitted he had run out of local listeners who were willing to sit through his yarns and often-repeated stories.

I found out a while back that the best way to be welcomed in a small town is to keep your mouth shut and put on your best I'm-a-good-listener face.

Looking around the small interior of Wichtown's only operating Main Street business kept me occupied for a short while. As I began to make my rounds of the small shop, the antique, tin silver-colored roof looked down on me. My mind and eyes were shelf shopping, trying to spot anything that might add a little local culture or color to my description of the setting.

Handmade decoys, signed by an area artist, initially caught my eye. But they soon lost out to the cute little miniature witches, riding thin, delicate brooms made of wooden twigs and straw. Two rows, totaling about three dozen of the small, eerie figures, filled the top of one store shelf. They were directly above a batch of fresh bread and rolls located on the shelf below.

Beside the creatures a hand-lettered sign stated, "Wichtown Festival Souvenirs."

"They's good luck charms!" shouted the sandwich maker, looking over the counter where she was creating a South Jersey version of an Italian sub. "Keeps the haints away!" she added,

explaining the usefulness of the little creatures. "Sell a hellava lot
of them in Hallows Month, during our yearly fest. We get everybody dressed up like witches all over town, here. From one
enda Main to the other. Gotta big contest and all. Ya outta come
down and see it. Come back then. Lotsa folks—locals and gawk-
ers—all over the place. Flashing pictures. Even got a float in the
parade with the winnin' witch. Real, real busy. Not like today.
Dead as dry dirt this time a year."

I nodded, smiled and turned to head back to my table and
cooling cup of tea, still waiting for Darryl to arrive. I glanced at
my watch. It was 3:30. He had told me to meet him at 3 o'clock,
and I was beginning to get upset. After all, the drive from
Maryland had taken nearly 90 minutes and I wouldn't be getting
back home until after dark.

"No sense getting all twisted an' outta shape!" the sub lady
called out to me. "Darryl, he ain't never been on time in his life.
Probably be late for his own damn buryin'. Ain't nothin' to do
with you. Jest the way he is. Independent. Goofy, really."

Surprised, I turned toward her, about to ask how she knew I
was becoming impatient, waiting for Darryl, when the door
opened. The bell attached to the wooden door announced the
entrance of the hour's second visitor into the Old General Store.
Along with a gust of wind, in blew the old waterman/farmer/
decoy carver/volunteer fireman/constable.

Like noise escaping from a whirlwind, a shouting form of
conversation erupted from one end of the old building to the
other.

"Shut the damn door, ya old fossil!" directed the annoyed
lady owner.

"Only if ya shut yer damn trap, ya ugly bag a bones!" the
visitor replied in a voice doubly loud.

"This fella's been wearin' out my pine boards waitin' on ya,
Darryl! No way to treat a visitor. Damn well knows we don't git
many this timea year."

My guide shook his head and rolled his eyes as he
approached my table. Since I was the only one in the store, he
had no trouble realizing I was his man.

Before he could speak to me, the shrill voice from the sub
counter continued, "Tell him to buy one of my witchy woos, for
good luck. Can't leave town without it."

Darryl pumped my hand as he used his other paw to dust himself off with his red baseball cap. Whispering, he said, "She's a bit daft, that's for sure. Her old man an' me worked the Delaware for years. If ya ask me, he shoulda drowned her like a sick kitten when she was born, but like a damn fool he kept her an' raised her best he could. Only way he got away from her screamin' and yappin' was in a box. An' I swear he was smilin' all the way down to hell. Why, livin' with Satan's better than listenin' to that screechin' and howlin' all day and night long."

I offered a knowing smile as I stood up still shaking his hand. It was strong, calloused, a result of more than six decades working the land and water.

Abruptly, he turned, headed toward the voice and, as he passed the souvenir shelf, grabbed an item and stopped in front of the owner.

"Here's a damn dollar, Jezzy!" he snarled. "Take it and get the hell offa my back. You're like a damn monkey. Man can't even have a conversation without your orderin' an' bossin'. Damn annoyin'."

"They's TWO dollars, ya cheap bastard!"

The sound of Darryl's solid palm connecting with the flat counter caused a cannon-like blast that flew through the store.

"I know ya buy them damn witches for two-bits and makes a good 'nough profit. So it's one damn dollar you'll git from me and be damn t' hell thankful, too."

Surprisingly, there was no retort, no return salvo from the shop owner. By the time I looked up, Darryl, his face red as a Jersey tomato, stomped past me, shoved a tiny "witchy woo" into my hand and snarled, "Let's git us the hell outta here. Gettin' t' be dark soon. Can't go out there when it's dark."

I followed him through the door, and we walked a few paces before he stopped and turned. The wind had picked up and was blowing at a good clip. The chill of the fresh air felt good, but wasn't enough to calm his mood.

"That damn witch is gonna git hers one day for sure, she is," he said. Then he suddenly stopped talking and laughed, as if he had more to say but thought better of sharing his homicidal plans with a complete stranger. "That's the trouble with women," he said, smiling, "Lord gave 'em a mouth. Hell. You's too young to recall, but in the old days damn females stayed at home, havin' kids, makin' meals. Got dressed up on Sundays and kept outta a man's way. That's when we was kings. Damn good days they was. Now, boy, them women got them an attitude—an' a big oversize mouth to go with it. They say there's three things that takes a woman's attractive nature away—book learnin', their own bank account an' a quick tongue. Understand?"

I paused, realizing that a part of what Darryl said made quite a bit of sense. Unfortunately, before I could agree, my opportunity for male bonding had passed.

"No," Darryl said wearily, "you's from a different time. Can't comprehend the way it was. Got no clue."

"Sure," I said. "Like in the '50s," I added.

Shaking his head and spitting on the sidewalk, he stared me in the eyes, sneered, and said in a whispered growl, "Yeah, boy. Like in them '50s. Them good ol' 1850s. Lets us get goin' Gonna git dark in a hour. "

Seated in the passenger seat of Darryl's Ford pickup, I watched the passing countryside as he talked about days long gone, when a man could fish all day, hunt coon all night, grab a few breakfast beers at the general store and do it all over again—plus catch and kill enough to make a decent enough living.

I pulled out the witchy woo he had given me from my jacket pocket. Thanking him for the gift, I asked, "What's with the witch stuff?"

"Co-mer-ci-a-lee-za-shion," he replied, swerving on the two-lane road to avoid a deep pothole.

I nodded, waiting for more. I had learned long ago, silence is sometimes better than asking a follow-up question.

"Wichtown for witches. Get it?" he explained. "Around 20 years back, somebody wakes up one day and dreams up this grand idea that the town could make itself some money if it played up the witch in Wichtown. So, they gets all excited an' hold this yearly parade an' costume contest. They go all out, got special printed-up T-shirts and candy apples an' all. They sell them little wooden critters you got there as souvenirs to them out-a-towners, who flock down here like geese in heat to catch themselves a peek at a real witch in good ol' Wichtown. All a game, really. But seems to work. So what's the harm?"

"So there are no real witches in town?" I asked, tossing out the humorous comment as an innocent remark to pass the time.

Darryl slowed the truck's speed, pulled off the paved road and headed up a dirt path that was only wide enough for one vehicle to pass through. Pointing beyond the windshield, he said, "We gotta go out an' take down the chain, then it's only 'bout a mile in the woods, The Olden Place. On past the clearin' and out 'round near beside the ol' crick."

As we each exited opposite doors and headed toward the chain wrapped around the wooden stakes, Darryl said, "We got us a few left in town, maybe six, seven—real witches, so they claim. Not many more than that. Nobody knows for sure. But not many, all on accounta the gene pool's down real low now'-days. Don't know how many more years they's got. Even livin' up to three times normal they can't hold on forever. Need fresh blood, but ain't there to be had."

I pulled on one end of the thick, rusted chain to relieve pressure on the hook as Darryl detached the twisted links and let the swinging metal barrier fall into the dirt. Staring at him, I said, "What are you talking about?"

He turned, smiled and answered calmly, "Ya asked about the witches in town. I jest answered ya."

Walking toward him, I asked him to provide a bit more detail about the gene pool and lack of fresh blood.

As if responding to the price of crops in season, Darryl calmly said that during the witch trials in Salem, and the subsequent executions, similar purges occurred throughout the other colonies. In southern New Jersey and Maryland, women suspected as witches were hung, stoned and in several cases had their homes and animals burned at the stake.

"We got us a place up north called Gallows Hill," he said. "They stretched the necks of more than two dozen women, young and old, an' that sent the rest into hidin'. Anyway, ya kill off a couple to three or four dozen witches all of a sudden like, an' that sure puts a crimp in the trainin' program for the young, up an' comin' witches-to-be. Plus, if you become a dead witch hangin' from a tree trunk, I don't care how good them magical potions of yours was, you ain't gonna have no more young ones. So, that's the gene pool story. Ended real sudden, cut down on the offspring. Now, like I said, we gotta few, like Jezzy—Jezebel, at the store you was in. But, they's gettin' up in years, and with that comes a bad attitude. So they ain't the kinda females that are gonna attract no suitors. Hell, would you wanna court that screechin' hellcat?"

I didn't answer.

"Right!' Darryl said, leaning on the wooden post that had held the end of the chain barrier. "No way I'd have me no child with that poor excuse for a female bein'. Even her best love potion mixed in a free shot of straight whiskey wouldn't get me to head off with her to the hayloft, no way. So, they's dyin' off. Plus, the witch wanna-bes who come down from Philly for witch potion lessons, they don't have them any natural talent. They's interested, but it ain't in them the natural way. It's like tryin' to turn a plow horse into a Kentucky Derby winner. Won't work, no way. Ain't got that genuine stuff. An' no matter how many workshops they take, they ain't gonna be a bonafied witch. An' nobody's gonna convince me otherwise. Understand?"

This time I nodded quickly.

"Good," Darryl said, and headed back to the truck. "Let's go. Olden Place's a waitin'."

We followed the dirt trail between a few hundred acres of untended fields resting for the season. Nearby, a thick stretch of forest was dark and dense.

About a half-mile in the distance, looking out in a two o'clock direction from the nose of the pickup, was an elevated mound with a stand of trees surrounded and consumed by think brush.

"That's it," Darryl announced. "Olden Place."

I was not surprised that its existence was a secret, for nothing indicated the slightest clue of the presence of the long-forgotten cemetery.

Darryl parked the truck in the road and we walked uphill toward the top of the mound. The sun was still up, but within a half hour would fall behind the treetops of the woods we had just driven past. In less than an hour darkness would begin to surround us and the long lost graves.

"They's in here," Darryl announced proudly. Then laughing, he added, "Hell, not like they was gonna go anywhere, since they been here for more than 250 years."

I smiled and pointed the beam of my flashlight into the waist-high thicket of briars and wild saplings. I could see crooked shapes of stones, some rounded, some irregular and jagged, in the distance, about 30 feet away.

Darryl called out, directing me to follow him and head toward the crick.

When I caught up to my guide, he was standing beside a wide, winding waterway, framed on all sides by tall, pale yellow marsh grass. It was a spectacular sight, with old trees leaning off the edges of the shore, half falling into the water.

A scattering of birds flew over the smooth water surface, nipping at bugs, while a flock of geese, at a much higher elevation, passed overhead. I understood why this peaceful sight had been chosen as a final resting place for the forgotten souls hidden among the tree trunks and thorn bushes.

"This here's called Graveyard Gut," Darryl said, "a little crick offa the Conaghensky, Nobody but me, a handfula old fools who can't talk or think no more, and now you, know what's out here. Nobody else knows or cares to know, either."

He pointed southwest, toward the Delaware River and the setting sun.

"They used to bring 'em up here by boat, they did. Quicker an' smoother than usin' the roads. The lead boat would be haulin' the box. All smooth wood with handles for the pallbearers. Have one fella with a pole standin' up front, on the bow, an' another in the back there, to steady the body so it won't fall ina crick.

"Then," he added, looking into the depths of the water as if he could see a long gone floating burial procession rounding the meandering stream. "Then, the

Neglected tombstones in an overgrown section of Olden Place along Graveyard Gut

family would float on in right behind—single file. The mother an' wife a cryin'. Their sobbin' and wailin' travelin' like fingernails on a blackboard over them marshes, probably disturbin' the sleepin' bastards behind us. Announcin' that they had company a comin'."

I noticed that darkness was steadily moving in our direction as we stood there, beside the forgotten resting place of long-rotting bodies hidden under the trees and wild flowers.

Darryl continued to describe the phantom funeral flotilla. "Next, the friends, trailin' behind in their own craft, paying respects. Would be a couple a dozen boats in the ol' days, followin' in file, with lanterns on the front an' rear, both outta respect and sos they wouldn't run into each others."

I was about to tell him that it was getting late, when he turned to me and pointed to the ground, not far from my feet. The land stopped abruptly as if it had been claimed by the meandering movement of Graveyard Gut.

"They say the water's been comin' up and pullin' them in, takin' them away little by little," Darryl explained. "When I was a boy, Olden Place went on out there 'nother 20, even 30 feet. Now, less an' less bodies up here on the mound. But, maybe it's good that the gut pulls 'em in. Nobody on land wants to tend 'em no more. You an' me, we ain't gonna do it. Hell, this place is too far outta the way for even the teenagers to come and have drinkin' parties. Only company these poor dead bastards have is when a groundhog burrows down an' takes a nap in their rib cage. Heard tell that happ . . . . "

Suddenly, Darryl stopped, turned his head from side to side and nervously asked, "You hear that?"

A chill ran through my body, not the kind that passes quickly, but the type that goes to the core of the bone and lasts too long to ignore.

"No," I said, my voice almost a whisper.

Then I heard it, a distant wail, a moaning that seemed to be coming across the gut, the waterway whose surface had turned from sky blue to a quickly darkening gray. Darkness had reached the Olden Place, and we were frozen like statues, unable to walk away, for the cries continued and increased in volume.

Turning ever so slowly, Darryl looked downstream, toward the bend in Graveyard Gut, and raised his hand, instructing me to look in the direction of his pointing finger.

Accompanying the crescendo of wails, a reflection of light, attached to the tip of a black funeral boat, came into view. Across the center of the small craft rested a pale pine box. The letters "RIP" were crudely painted onto the base.

Two men in old clothing, reminiscent of an earlier time, stood at either end of the death vessel.

As a second boat–filled with black-cloaked mourners weeping, moaning and praying–materialized, I realized what I was witnessing and grabbed for Darryl's shoulder. But he had left my side and was racing toward his truck.

Without waiting for an invitation, I charged behind. But my eyes were drawn to frantic movement coming from the weeds and briars that covered Olden Place. More than a dozen figures, wearing ragged remnants of their former funereal finest, floated up from the earth and headed toward the shoreline, apparently eager to greet the arriving newcomer and guests.

As the temperature dropped at least 30 degrees, I remember the deathly images well:

Tall man in a tattered top hat with a broken brim.

Mud splattered on a younger woman's wedding gown.

Moss covered jacket and trousers hanging off a skeletal figure.

White shoes coated in mud floating toward the water.

Chalk-white skeleton face beneath a dark brown bonnet.

Crying baby, wearing brown-colored rags, crawling on all fours toward the waterway.

Like the clearly unforgettable experience of a very bad dream, each of my legs felt as if it weighed 500 pounds. My

A view of Graveyard Gut from the edge of the forgotten cemetery

limbs would not move, no matter how hard I tried to force them into motion. I was unable to distance myself from the phantom funeral.

With all my strength, I reached out with my right arm, trying to signal Darryl to wait. I screamed, but nothing came out of my mouth. His taillights were bright, but in no time they became so very small, like tiny penlight laser dots. Then, as if the batteries had no life left in them to give, the pink pinpoints were gone.

And I was left behind—alone in the Olden Place.

Well, not quite on my own.

In extra slow-motion, I turned and stared toward Graveyard Gut, where they all were gathering—the Top Hat Man, Muddy Shoe Boy. Skeletal Bride—plus the new arrivals in clothing that was in better condition.

The Dead Baby was still crawling at a steady pace, but now in my direction. So was the rest of the ghastly cast of corpses. Apparently, they didn't get much company and had decided that they didn't want me to leave.

Still and motionless, I tried to scream—but no sound escaped my mouth.

The icy chill had disappeared, replaced by a thick, hot sense of dread. My body was dripping with sweat. It was pouring down my back in rivulets. Beads of water were dripping off my upper lip.

The last thing I recall was the putrid stench of decomposing flesh, which became more pungent as they approached closer and surrounded me. Unable to breath or scream or move, I closed my eyes and knew that I would join them in Olden Place along Graveyard Gut—and no one would ever find me, for no one know where I was.

Then my world went from Technicolor horror to the safety and peacefulness of black.

My wife said I had been sick, totally unconscious, for three days.

I don't even remember being rushed to the hospital in an ambulance or later being driven home by my son.

I had no memory of nurses or medications or doctors in white coats or being x-rayed and examined and washed and fed and clothed.

I had been gorked out for three days—they said.

They explained that they had found me on the floor beside my desk, a telephone in my hand. The other party must have gotten tired of waiting for me to come back to life and hung up.

My son, the official family nurse, told me one doctor guessed I had suffered a stroke, another couldn't offer an explanation, a third refused to say anything. I think they were more confused than they thought I was—but I wasn't. I know where I had been. The only problem was no one believed me, because they thought I had been in the hospital in front of them.

When I told them I had been interviewing a farmer in New Jersey, in Wichtown to be specific, they nodded, agreeing with me for the first few days the way totally sane people pacify a certified mental patient.

A week after I was home, and finally getting up and around on my own, with the use of a walker, they started to try to convince me that I had not been to Wichtown. They said that there was no such place and that I had never called or met or spoken to a man named Darryl Nebs. They told me with complete conviction that he didn't exist.

They showed me a New Jersey state map, explaining that there was no such place in the index or on the map itself.

During the follow-up doctor visit, my physician listened patiently to my description of Graveyard Gut, the stench of the floating bodies, the pinprick taillights of the Ford pickup as it drove off and left me behind and the overgrown bushes covering Olden Place. Then, as if she hadn't heard a word I had said, she told me and my wife and son, who where there to be sure I wasn't committed to a nut house, that some things seem so vivid in dreams or while we are under sedation, that it might take a little time for the lifelike memories to pass.

"Just be patient," she said.

"There, there," my wife added, patting my shoulder.

"You'll be just fine, Dad," my son assured me, offering a forced smile.

I nodded, agreed. Decided that was the only thing I could do.

Of course, I wasn't a complete idiot. I smiled back at them, accepting their soothing, lying comments on the outside and knowing if I insisted on standing by the truth they would take away my car keys and MAC card. So what if no one would ever believe me.

I didn't care. I knew the truth.

Perhaps I had been transported into another dimension, or been beamed into a mother ship and sent to a place where people we can't see live and exist and function.

I don't have the precise answer, but I have a feeling I'll be going back to Wichtown.

You see, I know there's more to all of this than my family members could possibly understand.

And the answer is out there, at Olden Place and in that strange "Old-Time General Store."

I know, because on my desk, right beside the keyboard I am using this minute to write about my experience, is a cute little witchy woo creature. It has tiny red, pinpoint eyes, and on the bottom of its base it is a message: "To Ed from Darryl."
I have no idea how I brought it back with me, or how it got here, no clue at all.

But I do know it's real, as genuine as Darryl and Jezzy and the creepy cadavers that are sleeping right this very minute beside Graveyard Gut, somewhere outside of Wichtown, New Jersey. And if you ever go through that town, and you're able to leave, drop me a line.

Bigg Lizz
Guardian of the Gold

Dorchester County, Eastern Shore of Maryland

Her name was, and still is, Bigg Lizz. In fact, she's so big that we spell it with two "g's" and two "z's," out of respect and recognition of her extraordinary life, untimely death and apparent immortality. For some believe that Bigg Lizz still exists and roams the swamps and forests of Dorchester County, Maryland, even though she died about 150 years ago.

The story of Bigg Lizz has been told in country stores, repeated in barbershops, written up for school papers and documented in newspapers and books about regional folklore.

One of the most well-known versions of the tale can be found in *Shore Folklore, Growing Up With Ghosts, 'N Legends, 'N Tales, 'N Home Remedies* by The Old Honker Thomas A. Flowers.

I never had the pleasure of meeting Dr. Flowers, but I spoke to him once on the phone. We exchanged pleasantries and I told him that his book had a very special place in my private library of Delmarva literature. The book, which is a must for any regional book collector, contains wonderful stories and tales, history and humor among its more than 250 pages of text and photographs.

One of the chapters in Flowers' book details the story of Bigg Lizz.

This account of the Bigg Lizz tale has been assembled from various sources, including stories in books and magazines plus verbal versions of the famous Delmarva folktale.

During the Civil War, citizens throughout the Delmarva Peninsula were divided. Some were loyal to the North while others had equally strong sentiment for the Southern cause. Neighbors were at odds over the issue of slavery and states' rights, and members of the same family who had opposite views found some sons wearing blue uniforms and others wearing gray.

While Maryland remained in the Union, many of her citizens, on both sides of the Chesapeake Bay, fought and supported the Confederacy. Evidence exists today of the legacy of Maryland's sons of the Eastern Shore who fought for the Rebel cause. In small church graveyards as far north as Elkton and Rising Sun, the inscription CSA—indicating Confederate States of America—can be found on tall granite monuments and small weathered tombstones.

In Dorchester County, far to the south of the Pennsylvania border and the north-south dividing section of the Mason Dixon Line, a wealthy plantation owner worked secretly as an agent for representatives of CSA President Jefferson Davis in Richmond.

Sacks of gold and silver coin were delivered to the plantation where Bigg Lizz worked, and "The Master" considered her one of his most dependable and hardworking slaves.

What he eventually found out was that Bigg Lizz was a spy for the Union. Since he had treated her quite well, The Master was immensely disappointed to learn that she reported her owner's activity to federal troops on a regular basis.

One night, when his chest was filled and could not contain any more gold and coin, The Master called for Bigg Lizz. She was a large black woman with powerful muscles, and he directed her to lift the wooden chest and place it in the back of his wagon. Together they rode in darkness on a hot summer night into the depths of the area known as Green Briar Swamp.

Once there, The Master tossed Bigg Lizz a shovel and told her to dig a hold deep enough to hide the large treasure chest.

As Bigg Lizz burrowed deeper, less and less of her body could be seen emerging from the growing hole. Up and down she went, over and over. The rhythm of her powerful body took on a steady beat.

In the shovel went, down the body followed, up the head came, into the air the dirt flew.

In the shovel went, down the body followed, up the head came, into the air the dirt flew.

The pace was so regular that The Master began to tap his foot to the steady repetition.

In the shovel went, down the body followed, up the head came, into the air the dirt flew.

One. Two. Three. Four.

One. Two. Three. Four.

When the hole was approaching the desired depth, he ordered Bigg Lizz to dig just a little deeper, to be sure that varmints wouldn't disturb the chest and its contents.

Finally, the freshly carved crypt was done to The Master's satisfaction, and he ordered Lizz out of the hole. His glove covered hand pointed to the massive box, and he told her to place it in the bottom of the pit.

That done, Lizz resumed her shovel work, standing on level land, not far from The Master and his wagon. Her body was at the edge of the hole overtop the swampy grave.

Again her actions took an a rhythmic style, bending over and twisting as she shoved the tip of the tool into the tall pile of damp earth and released its contents into the hole.

Turn, bend, dip, pull, toss.

Turn, bend, dip, pull, toss.

Turn, bend, dip, pull, toss.

The Master began tapping his toe again, smiling as he observed her steady pace, the strong muscles of her body at work, the high level of concentration.

He was proud that she was his, that he owned her. A better slave he could not have acquired, but then he shook his head, obviously bothered by what had to be.

Busy with her task, Bigg Lizz did not notice The Master, standing on the wagon deck,

Bigg Lizz and the lost treasure are hidden in the Eastern Shore swamp.

directly behind her body. A large tobacco knife, about three feet long and razor sharp, was clutched tightly in his hands.

As her body bent forward, then raised itself into an upright position, Bigg Lizz's massive sweating head was only a few feet from The Master's waist. He tapped his toe, getting into the rhythm of the moment, her rhythm, her steady pace.

Then, when her head was highest, closest to the level of his belt line, he timed his motion perfectly. In one flowing, smooth and rapid motion, he pulled back both arms and directed the silver blade of the razor-edge tobacco knife forward, catching Bigg Lizz unaware.

A strange look of surprise was frozen on her face as the round, full head flew into the air and landed with a "thunk" against a nearby tree. The headless corpse, which didn't yet know it was dead, took three erratic steps forward, tumbling in a heap into the death hole. Within seconds, a headless Bigg Lizz ceased to function, and the lifeless mass rested atop the chest of Confederate gold.

With the crypt conveniently prepared and the gold safely hidden, The Master adjusted his riding gloves and began to fill in the hole. This was one physical task he could trust no one to do.

Slowly, the remains of Bigg Lizz were covered with swamp dirt. The Master prepared to return to his plantation house, satisfied that only he knew the site of his treasure chest. Laughing aloud, he thought how clever it was for him to leave the slave's body sprawled atop the chest. With satisfaction, he compared Bigg Lizz's eternal role to the ancient pirate practice—where a murdered crew member was tossed atop a treasure chest to safeguard its contents for eternity.

Then he remembered the woman's head, which had rolled off and hit the moss covered tree. Stopping his horses, he turned in his seat and thought for a moment about going back and retrieving it. But in the dark it would be impossible to locate. Besides, he convinced himself, there was a good chance the tasty face had been carted off by a wild boar or fox.

Laughing, he thought of Bigg Lizz being devoured, and all evidence of his buried treasure and the murder in the marsh would be gone before daylight.

It was nearly three in the morning when he arrived at the front of his mansion. The Master shouted for Lucas, his blacksmith slave, to take the horses and wagon to the barn. Even though it was late, Lucas appeared within moments. Everyone knew it was not a good idea to keep The Master waiting. Quite tired from a full evening of stressful activity, The Master was in bed by 3:15 a.m. and fast asleep moments later.

After what only seemed to be a few seconds, he was awakened by a scratching sound that seemed to be coming from a corner of the room.

He turned in his bed, pulled the pillow close around his head and ears to block out the sound, and tried to return to his much needed sleep.

But rest would not be his that night.

The annoyance was louder this time, and sounded closer, much closer. It was as if the scratching was coming from beneath his mattress.

Sitting up in his bed, The Master shouted, "What is making such a noise!"

No one answered, but he noticed that the temperature in his room had dropped dramatically. It had been a humid summer night, but in his room it felt like the winter winds had entered through the open third-floor window.

Jumping from his bed to shut the window, his bare feet reacted to the bitter cold of the floor.

"What is this?" he wondered aloud, but he never reached the window. From the corner of his eye, he noticed two, small red dots of light. They were about four feet off the floor and heading toward him. As they came closer, a huge figure of a woman in familiar clothing, worker's clothing, slave clothing—came into view.

Bigg Lizz had returned and emerged from the shadows. Her headless body glided across the room, toward The Master, who was moving backwards at a very rapid pace. In the dead woman's left hand was her head, which she held by her hair.

The red glowing eyes seemed to direct the rest of Bigg Lizz's immense dead body in the direction it should go. She had no trouble following her prey around the mansion's large master bedroom.

In the ghost's right hand was a rather impressive tobacco knife. The Master knew that its blade was sharp, for he had used it earlier in the evening with good results. However, now the bright silver metal was coated with dried, black-red bloodstains—the blood of Bigg Lizz, who had come from the swamp to take her revenge.

The Master was a smart man, knew more than most. After all, he owned and operated a successful plantation, and he had convinced his Rebel associates to trust him with their personal wealth. So he must have known that his death would occur in a matter of moments, and that there would be no reasoning with or mercy from the ghoul of Bigg Lizz.

But logic does not always prevail in times of strife and danger. The Master pleaded and cried, shouted and cursed, but nothing swayed the ghost from her goal. Terrified at the thought of spending eternity without his head, the Master jumped onto a chair and dove out the window, crashing to his death on the ground three stories below.

His body was found the following morning and he was buried on the grounds of his plantation.

The chest of gold and Bigg Lizz's head and body were never located. According to legend, her banshee remains in the swamp, somewhere in the area of Bucktown, south of Cambridge near DeCoursey's Bridge. She's there to protect the gold, a solitary sentinel standing watch forever.

Treasure hunters with sophisticated metal detectors have visited the area searching for the lost gold. They say they're not interested in Bigg Lizz. Some even laugh when they hear stories about her being the guardian of the gold. But they are careful to work only during daylight.

Area high school students, who say she's the product of an active imagination, have organized outings to locate the swamp monster. But they only make one excursion into the forests and never return. When they speak about the experience, they admit the swamp is eerie, very troubling, not a nice place to play or explore.

But others still go there, to look

There are even reports that Bigg Lizz has moved. One story tells of her head, appearing in the Chesapeake Bay, circling small pleasure boats at night and calling out for help, asking to be pulled from the water.

Another version says that the old girl has taken the treasure with her, and that she now sits on the chest in the middle of the

Pocomoke Forest. But that story seems a bit far-fetched, not as believable as the original tale.

But who's to say what's true and what's not, what's real and what's imagined, what's the way it is and what's what you want it to be?

The facts are these: Bigg Lizz was real. She was murdered. The Master is dead. The gold remains yet to be found—and even in the 21st century, strange and terrifying things still happen deep in the swamps and forests on the Eastern Shore of Maryland.

Wolfman on the Wharf

Atlantic City, New Jersey

He's always alone, moving slowly along the Boardwalk, feeding popcorn to the gulls while sitting on a bench that usually faces the ocean, eating a sandwich at a booth beside the window in a seashore diner or parked with his feet dangling over the edge of a deserted dock or pier—usually at night—while the sea crashes against the pilings 20 feet below.

That's where I caught up with him, at a wharf overgrown with weeds that had not been used commercially for many years, at the far north end of the world's most famous Boardwalk, in Atlantic City, New Jersey.

But let me backtrack and explain how this all started.

In addition to my books on ghosts and regional folklore, I also write stories based on interviews with people who do unusual or outstanding things. This would include the woman who dresses up ceramic ducks, which are bolted to her front porch, and changes their attire each week; and the man with a collection of 10,000 license plates from around the world stacked in special racks in his basement; then there's the fellow who is obsessed with finding a local version of Bigfoot, which he swears travels up the East Coast, along the riverbeds and in the shadows of the shoulders of Interstate 95.

In New Jersey, along Route 40, one of the nation's oldest highways, are several sites that I have targeted for serious investigation. Two at the top of my list are the Purple Penguin roadside ice cream store and Jug City, U.S.A., both located a short distance from "AC" one of the country's most famous gambling shrines.

I was discussing my latest quest, and at the same time searching for new leads, with a waitress during a late night meal at a Mays Landing diner. I learned a long time ago that diner people are a great source for finding out about local characters.

When the server asked me to describe what I was looking for, I said, "He or she has to be a bit of an oddball. Some people would say an eccentric, but that's too academic or stuffy sounding for me. I want to talk to a person with personality, who does something other people don't do or overlook and, most importantly, who really doesn't care what other people think. A real character with a capital 'C.' And it would help a lot if he's nice. I don't like to write about creeps or people who think they're God's gift to the world."

The waitress paused, nodded, began to take away my empty plate and said, "I think I've got a guy for you. But, he's hard to find and definitely way out there. As for charming, I can't vouch. But if he would talk to you, it would be worth your time. He would be perfect for a chapter in your book. He's an oddball, but harmless, really. He's in here once or twice a month, doesn't talk much, just orders, eats and stares out the window. Always at night and always alone. But he's got a story, a real good one. I'll have to ask Lou the Cook how to get to him. He knows him pretty good, I think."

She disappeared through one of those swinging doors that open before the person gets to it. Must have had some kind of electric eye gizmo or something nearby. About five minutes later, a guy arrived. It was Lou the Cook in a white T-shirt, tall chef hat and tattoo decorations of birds and spiders all over his arms and neck.

"You wanna meet Wolfman?"

I looked up at the waitress who had appeared by the cook's side. "I don't know his name. Is that the one?" I asked the woman, and she nodded back to me.

"He's a real irregular regular, if ya know what I mean."

I nodded and waited for more.

Lou the Cook continued. "There ain't no schedule for him. Just comes in whenever. If I took your name, he's never gonna call you. So no sense in that. An' I ain't gonna put gettin' you and him hooked up on my back. Hell, I got plenty do deal with in this place and at the trailer. Besides, what's in it for me?"

I realized he was expecting a payment, but that wasn't going to happen. If I had to pay for every bizarre lead I'd been offered, I wouldn't have been able to afford to eat in his diner. So I shrugged my shoulders and shook my head from side to side, indicating "nothing."

Tossing his hands up in the air, Lou the Cook turned and snarled, "I figured as much. Another freebster wantin' somethin' for nothin'. Hell with this!" In less than a half-dozen steps he returned to the room where he went to his job of making and mixing and matching food orders delivered on little slips of paper by the more friendly, people-oriented waitresses. I was glad I had finished my feast, for I'm sure he would have spit in my soup and sandwich if I had just arrived.

"Too bad," the waitress said. I noticed the word "Molly" was inked on her faded nametag.

As she pushed a damp rag wiping down the table, I asked her, "What's this Wolfman's claim to fame, anyway? Does he howl or have fur all over his face? What's the deal?"

Still leaning down forward, she paused and glanced quickly over her shoulder. When she was sure Lou the Cook wasn't anywhere in sight, Molly whispered, "He believes he's been abducted by aliens. Swears by it. Don't say I told you, but I'd check with the cops in Margate or AC. They'll probably be able to tell you where to find him. But don't say I sent you. I don't want Lou to know."

"No problem," I said, thanking her with a decent tip as I slid out of my booth and headed for home.

A week later, on my next trip to the Jersey Shore, I knew I'd place locating Wolfman on my to-do list.

The desk cop at the Margate City Police Station didn't have any idea of the person I was seeking. But he was young, hadn't been on the job long and had arrived with his family two months before from Kansas. (Now there was a story, but I didn't have time to become sidetracked.) He suggested I head south and hit a few of the constables with more years of experience in the smaller beach towns.

I grabbed my map and did my own version of Al Albert's song "On the Way to Cape May," stopping at a half-dozen law enforcement headquarters along the South Jersey Coast.

In Avalon, I got the name of a retired officer who had locked up Wolfman more than once. He was out when I located his home, but I left him a note. (He never called.)

In Stone Harbor, two cops began laughing when I mentioned my subject's name and suggested I "camp out" on the sand and wait for a full moon. Through coughing and chuckles, they assured me Wolfman "was out there"—in more ways than one.

It was in Sea Isle City and Wildwood that I pieced together a story that more understanding members of the beach cleaning patrols offered.

Apparently, Wolfman's unique name had been acquired because of reports describing a solitary man, dressed in a heavy black fur coat, sitting out on the beaches at night along the South Jersey Shore—and all he would do is stare out at sea.

Someone looking at a photograph that had been taken one night at a distance, pointed to the dark fuzzy mass and suggested he was out there to "howl at the moon," hence the Wolfman identity was created.

Sightings of the man dressed in black began in 1995 and continued through early 2000. They stopped for about 18 months and started up again before the end of 2001.

Wolfman traveled the coastline, stopping at shore villages between Cape May and Long Beach Island. There was no schedule or systematic timing of his appearances. Initially, the police locked him up for vagrancy. However, when he kept returning and proved harmless, the officers in most of the towns ignored Wolfman the moment they recognized who he was.

"They knew he wouldn't give them no trouble," one beach cleaner told me, "so they just waved him off. They had bigger fish to fry, real troublemakers to deal with. Wolfman wasn't hurtin' nobody, so they let him do his thing."

"Which is?" I asked.

"Which is," the guy said, "starin' at the freakin' beach in the dark of night. Now, how the hell can that hurt somebody? Does that bother you in any little way at all?"

I shook my head indicating "No."

"Right. Me neither. So they let 'em do his thing. They let him watch the stars an' water an' moon, and be happy. After all, that's all you can see out here at night. Right?

"I guess so," I agreed. But later I would find out I was wrong.

Two months passed until I sat down beside Wolfman on the northernmost pier in Atlantic City. One lead led to another that hit a dead end and caused me to start over again. I almost gave up, but forced myself to give it a little more time. Luckily, I was home to receive an anonymous call from a helpful Atlantic City police officer who said Wolfman was in the area and would "probably" be on watch that night.

I made the two-hour ride to AC. Had dinner and waited until nightfall. At 6:30 on a relatively mild February night I left the comfort and excitement of the Showboat Hotel and Casino and headed north along the Boardwalk.

There wasn't much traffic. I passed a guy who had been playing the saxophone for tips, but he was packing it up as the wind got stronger. Two winos were arguing under the edge of the boards over a bottle of booze. Other than that it was just me and the dark and the ocean and wind.

Even though the temperature was in the 40s, the wind was blowing steadily off the ocean. To my right I could hear the crashing waves pounding the beach.

Wind and water combined and lowered the temperature dramatically. It wasn't long before the chill of the winter night cut through my coat and burned the exposed skin on my face.

I pulled my hood tighter around my head and looked toward the ocean.

In what seemed like mid air, above the level of the sea, I noticed a yellow beam. It looked like a flashlight, and its illumination showed off a silhouette of a man—sitting at the end of a long, deserted, dilapidated pier.

I walked faster, to make sure he didn't get away. The physical activity of my body movement generated some warmth.

When I reached the spot where the pier met the Boardwalk, I pulled out a small flashlight and turned it on. It took me 10 minutes to get to the end of the dock, carefully avoiding holes caused by broken boards and rotted sections of the pier's flooring.

At the end, calmly facing the wild winds charging in from the ocean, sat Wolfman, clothed in black, with a battery operated heater and lantern directed toward his body.

"I heard you were coming," he said, not turning. His voice was calm, relaxed, even kind and inviting.

"You did?" I said, adding, "Mind if I sit down?"

"Go ahead," he replied, still not looking at me, "just don't block the heat. I'll be here a while and need to keep warm."

"How long?" I asked, shuffling into my seat that I hoped was safe and secure.

"I'll be here all night. Until daylight peeks over the horizon," he said. "Unless they come and take me off again. Then I don't know when I'll be back. They had me for a year once, 19 months, actually. Usually, it's only for a few hours or a day or two."

I waited, afraid to ask him to explain his comment but eager for any sort of answer. After a long 20 silent seconds, I whispered, "Who took you away?"

He turned and looked my way for only a moment. Since a cloth ski mask covered every part of his face except his eyes and lips, I could not see any facial reaction. But I could sense he was smiling when he replied, "Reptilians, of course. Although, I'm hoping it's the Grays that appear, instead."

"Why's that?" I wondered.

Still staring at the black mass of water that meshed with the darkness of the night sky, he replied, "Because they're nicer, more benevolent, not as evil. But I think they're all evil, to a degree. They have no benign agenda.

The deserted pier where I interviewed Wolfman

59

Domination is their ultimate objective, and they're progressing ahead of schedule." Then he paused, looked at me and added, "You don't know very much about this, do you?"

I didn't know what to say. I was afraid to admit that I only had a passing knowledge of the topic of UFOlogy, for fear he might tell me to take a long walk off a short pier—which could happen very easily under the circumstances. On the other hand, if I tried to fake it I could easily get caught in a lie, and that might end the interview that I had worked so hard to secure. So I did the best thing I could think of—I smiled and remained silent.

Thankfully, Wolfman seemed satisfied with my apparent ignorance and said, "Don't worry, I will tell you the entire story. It may take all night, but if you want to stay, all you have to do is listen. I spend so much time alone, waiting for them, it nice to have company for a change. You can be my diversion. Also," he added with a chuckle, "I haven't had any luck attracting their attention for several months. Your presence may help bring them back, and we both might go up to the Mother Ship together. Then you'll discover more than you ever dreamed you would learn from me."

I left the awkward smile on my face, frozen in place because my muscles were beginning to stiffen and I didn't know how to react to his last comment. I didn't think it was a joke. He was serious. This guy thought he had really been the victim of the command, "Beam me up, Scotty." Plus, he was out on a ice-coated wharf waiting to be picked up for a return trip to the heavens, sort of like the way people in New York stand on a corner and flag down a cab. Only they're more successful—thank God.

While I had no desire to end up on a lab table surrounded by little green men with almond eyes and long skinny fingers shoving tubes up my whatever, I was not going to be run off or put off by Wolfman's little game. I stayed the night, listened and learned about his bizarre life. And the following morning, as the sun finally rose over the horizon, I accompanied him to the Boardwalk. We shook hands, and I watched him walk away with his blanket and battery-powered heater in tow.

I took no notes that night. My fingers couldn't move, so I stuffed my hands deep inside my coat pockets. Besides, the wind would have ripped my notebook pages away. My tape recorder would have been useless, for the howling gales would have carried off Wolfman's comments before they traveled the short distance from his lips to the microphone.

All I have is the memory of that long, cold and fascinating evening on the wharf.

This is what I recall.

Some people think there is a close connection among ghosts, angels and aliens (as in UFO—unidentified flying objects). Where one category of paranormal beings ends and another begins is the focus of much talk among those who dabble in the business. But no one has ever come up with tangible proof verifying the existence of any of the three entities. So confirming their connection or relationships is another, more involved, mystery that will go unsolved and remained mired in speculation, opinion and the hazy area of "what ifs" and "maybes."

But on the topic of alien-being existence, there are tens of thousands of people like Wolfman, who are certain they exist, because, as he told me, he has been "among them."

"They took me away and kept me with them for more than a year, nearly a year and a half," he said, getting right to the highpoint of his extraterrestrial contact experience. "I had been abducted since I was about seven. I learned that recently. The encounters with them increased in frequency when I was in my 20s. I'm 32 now. And it always came out of there," he added, pointing toward the ocean.

Now I found this rather interesting, since most UFOlogists and flying saucer experts claim alien visitors come from "outer space," that they are visitors from other planets located in solar systems with advanced civilizations far, far away. But Wolfman, my abduction expert of the evening with firsthand experience, assured me the creatures live beneath the ocean and use the sky for rapid travel across the globe.

"They're already here," he said. "They don't come here, they live here, under the water. That's why they haven't been caught or found, because everyone is directing the search into outer space. It's like using a metal detector to locate gold or buried treasure by holding it upside down and swinging it back and forth above your head, in the air. There is not a very good possibility that you will be celebrating the major find you are seeking if the object of your attention is hidden under the Earth and you are looking up at the sky. Private UFO agencies and volunteer organizations are collecting data from the sky—electronic signals and sightings of unusual aircraft, but they should be directing their focus and efforts toward the sea."

"Does the government know about this?" I wondered, and then almost immediately put my hand across my mouth for fear that I had asked a stupid or inflammatory question too soon in the interview.

Wolfman let out a howl. "ARE YOU SERIOUS?" he shouted, making me nearly fall off the pier. "It IS the government. They have Defense Department scientists and Navy and Air Force and Army technicians working on the alien ships. I have seen them, even talked to them. They are we and we are they. And it's all down there, under the surface of the sea, but no one will bother to listen. But that's because they already know."

During the following 20 minutes, Wolfman explained that his recent 19-month sabbatical with the creatures from Atlantis or, wherever he claimed they were, had taken place without his knowledge. Basically, he didn't even know he was gone for such a long period of time until he had come back.

"I knew I had been beamed up," he said. "After it happens to you more than a hundred times, you can't not know. But I assumed it was only a normal spontaneous/unscheduled transport, lasting only for a day or two. I never imagined it could have lasted a year and a half. I went into one of my regular diners and the owner said he thought I had died. He said it in a funny, joking manner. When I asked him to explain, he said I hadn't been in for more than a year, adding things like, didn't I like the food and had I moved away, and all that.

"There was no reason that morning for me to check the date or day of the week. The previous day had been Wednesday, March 3. But when I picked up the newspaper, it said October 18. I hadn't noticed any dramatic weather change. It was relatively mild that year, and at the shore we don't have a lot of trees that indicate the seasonal color change. March and April are very much like September or October. It you weren't aware of the months, they could interchange comfortably.

"I started to tremble when I realized they had kept me for so long. I remember running out of the diner, racing under the Boardwalk and throwing up. I was in shock."

"Do you remember what happened down there?" I asked.

"Some, not all. It comes in bits and pieces, and then I try to connect it together. It's almost impossible to explain to someone who hasn't been abducted. But in a way, it's easier to describe today, because many people have seen the images of space ships in the movies *ET* and *Encounters of a Third Kind*, and even the show *X-Files* are part of a major, coordinated subliminal education program that the government is directing.

"While the appearance of the equipment and creatures are not precisely the same, to a fair degree it is an accurate representation of their advanced facilities and apparatus. Visually, you can have some idea of what I saw, because you've been exposed to the scenes in the motion picture entertainment venue.

"But, to describe the feeling of helplessness, of being restricted in captivity—not in a standard jail, where you are familiar with the physical setting and people and surroundings—but in an out-of-this-world environment, it is impossible to do justice to the setting. You are quite possibly trapped in another dimension or in a more advanced civilization. There is no way to relay the helplessness, the sense of absolute loss of power and entire lack of control. You become a serf to a race of masters, where even the lowest category of alien being is above you, is your ruler and superior. You are entirely dependent on the creatures' whims of largess or subject to their fits of irrational rage. During every second you are in fear of your continued existence, and you have no means of escape. Worst of all, there is nowhere to escape to. They have you as an experiment, a plaything. You are the equivalent of a laboratory rat until they are done with you. Only then—if you are among the fortunate survivors—you may be allowed to return. But you never know for how long. I could be here for a day, a week, forever. I know, however, if they decide to take me back they will find me and abduct me, no matter where I am at the time.

"I could be in a crowded room, surrounded by a hundred people, and they could cart me off with ease."

"How could that happen?"

Wolfman smirked, shook his head and pointed to the sky. "Shooting star," he said. "Lovely out here, although a bit cold this time of year. You never realize how much activity occurs above the ocean unless you stare at it for about 10 hours. The things you see."

He stopped, and then began to answer my earlier question, informing me that "location and access" were the two factors one needed to secure a person against his will.

"Finding me is never a problem," he said. "Somewhere in my body is an implant."

I assumed he was talking about a metal chip or alloy that the aliens could use to hone in on his whereabouts, but he corrected me.

"That's ancient history," he said. "DNA indentifiers have been installed in a satellite system that can read your molecular make-up, match it with a data bank and, within 10 minutes, the government can locate you anywhere in the world. Then, they can submit that information to laptops carried by 'sweeper' teams stationed all around the country. They can have you in the back of an unmarked van in no time, whisk you away to a safe house and alert the Mother Ship that you are in custody and packaged for delivery."

Wolfman explained that medical doctors, law enforcement officials and government employees, social workers and even religious leaders and their ministers were involved in a network that responded to demands by Alien Nation members.

"When you see an ambulance rushing through traffic, what's the first thing you think of?"

"How do I get out of its way," I said.

"But why is it there, where is it going?" Wolfman said, directing my thought process.

"Someone is ill or in need of emergency treatment."

"That," Wolfman said, "is true about 70 percent of the time. The other ambulance runs are pickups that are being held for transport and delivery to alien ships that are circling the globe constantly. You will find this additional information hard to believe. There are Mother Ships off the coast of the United States and every other major industrial nation, and some are housed at military bases and government testing facilities in underground chambers."

I couldn't contain myself any longer. "This sounds crazy. If I wrote about this, they would laugh at me."

"NO!" Wolfman said, pointing a finger at my head, and speaking in his most serious tone of the night. "If you write about this, they might come knocking at your door, asking you where you found this out. My advice is tell them you have a fertile imagination or you might get a ride to the big ship in the sky."

He didn't laugh and neither did I. It was colder than it had been. I peeked at my watch. It was nearly 4 o'clock in the morning. My feet were damp from the mist and surf that was smashing into the pilings below. I was beginning to think this was all a big fairy tale that was going nowhere.

"You think I'm insane, don't you?" Wolfman said. Before I could answer, he continued, "I come out here, on a deserted dock, waiting to be taken to someplace I don't want to go, freezing nearly to death. I'm a laughing stock of the Shore. I have no friends. I live in a one-room hovel in a hotel ready for condemnation, and I can't sleep during the day or night. I tell you the government is involved in the largest cover-up since the Kennedy Assassination—no, make that the Lincoln Assassination. Any sane man, like yourself, would consider all this unusual, to say the least. But more likely, this is comic book material. Am I correct?"

"Yes," I agreed.

"So now the question is: Do you believe me?"

"I don't know, probably not. At least not completely."

"Ah, a truthful answer from my Doubting Thomas," Wolfman said, laughing. "But now at least you have heard the bizarre story from someone who claims to have been there, been taken away, been probed and experimented on. So the next question is: What will you do with your knowledge, place it in a trite little book where the readers will think you made it up for their enjoyment during summer diversions?"

There was no answer coming from me at that moment. So Wolfman continued to talk, and that was good, since that was the reason I was there.

"Let me tell you how I discovered that I had been taken away. Let me explain how I became aware that the nightmares of big-eyed, pointy-headed, horrifying monsters were real.

"I awoke one day in my home, lying on the floor of my basement study, not far from my desk where I had been preparing my lectures for the following week's anthropology classes at the college. My wife and three little girls were outside, swimming in the pool. I could hear them in the distance as I began to raise my body from the carpeted floor.

"Thankfully, the door to the study had been closed tightly. No one had entered. My wife knew I did a lot of work late at night. For me it was the best time for research and planning. I have always been a night owl.

"As I rubbed my eyes, still tired from the exertion, I looked down and saw I was wearing someone else's clothes. The pajama pants were the loose, modern kind that fit both men and women. When I was teaching some of my students would even wear them to class. But these were pink, light pink with thin white stripes. That was all I had on. But I was fully clothed the night before, had not changed into my nightclothes, had been in my study all evening.

"My shoes were gone. My shirt was nowhere to be found. My pants, underwear, wallet were all missing. It was if I had been stripped and redressed. I ran upstairs to my bedroom, pulled off the strange pants and walked into the master bathroom, to clean up and take a shower. As I passed the mirror, I noticed marks all over my body—my chest, legs, back, thighs. Lines and circles were drawn with what looked like purple lipstick. Hurriedly, I washed it off and, while in the shower, I began to have flashbacks of the creatures in a laboratory and of huge black eyes close to my body, hovering over me. It was strange, but didn't make any sense. I hid the pants in the back of my closet, got dressed and went outside to spend the day with my family." Wolfman stopped, paused and said, quite slowly, "The strange thing is, after I began talking to my wife and children, the entire experience—of waking up on the floor and finding the strange clothing—disappeared from my mind . . . temporarily."

He said that was one of his last enjoyable days on or off the Earth, and Wolfman treasures the memory of that final perfect afternoon with his family.

Midway through the following week, late one evening while working alone in his study, he became increasingly agitated as

he started to recall the unexplainable experience that he had
been forced to endure during the previous weekend. Recalling
the hidden pajama pants, he ran upstairs, pulled them from the
hiding place and took them back to his study.

Turing and twisting them, he tried to find a clue, anything
that might help him explain their origin. Beneath the elastic
waistband he found a name and phone number inked into the
material. The next day, from his office at the university, he called
the number with a Pennsylvania area code.

"A woman answered," Wolfman said. "I was terrified to talk
to her. I mean, how was I going to explain how I had found her
number? But I didn't have to say very much. She almost cried
with joy when I told her why I was calling. She said, 'Don't say
anymore on the phone.' She lived in Philadelphia and called me
back on a cell phone, and we arranged to meet the coming
weekend. During that conversation in a restaurant along the
New Jersey Turnpike, Sally, that was her name, explained that
she had been abducted several times. She had learned a trick at
an abduction support group. They all agreed to place their name
and phone number somewhere hidden in their clothing, since
they also had awakened wearing clothes that weren't theirs. I
was the second person to call her in two years."

During their conversation, Sally described her experiences in
detail. Her story, and her descriptions of the events she had wit-
nessed, generated flashbacks of similar contacts Wolfman had,
and he began to remember them clearly. She invited him to
attend an abductees support group that met in various private
homes in Philly, but he declined.

"She couldn't help me," Wolfman said. "I had to get through
it alone. I'm still trying. That was seven years ago. My wife is
gone, remarried to a lawyer—any ex-husband's worst nightmare.
I am a walking, breathing albatross. I lost my job. My girls are
teenagers now, but they don't see me. My ex-wife and her new
husband made sure the girls know I'm crazy. There's a court
order directing me to stay away from their home. The only thing
I can do is send them a card on their birthdays. There is no way
for me to fight the law, I can't afford to now. That's the real reason I do this, sit out here in the cold like a deranged being.

"If I can get a good picture of that Mother Ship coming out
of the ocean one night, I mean a fine, indisputable image with

this expensive camera–that could be a serious step in proving that I'm not crazy, a start in getting my girls back, or at least convincing someone that I'm not a total fool.

"I have lost absolutely everything. Have nothing else to live for but to prove the creatures actually exist, that they are out there, and that the government is in on this one hundred percent. Anything I can find that will convince anyone at all about this situation, this very serious state of affairs, may help. Even a chapter in your little ghost book may be the critical turning point. It could get someone else who has seen something to step forward, or motivate them to find me and offer me some help or a clue.

"That's why I agreed to talk to you. In a way, I'm really being selfish. But, I can live with that. After what I've gone through, using you as a tool to tell my story is the least of my worries. I hope you write up what I told you accurately, but that's up to you, isn't it?"

Then Wolfman paused, laughed, and slapped my shoulder in a friendly way and added, "I have no control over what you or anyone else does." Then, shaking his head and looking me straight in the eye, he added, "Hell. I haven't had control over very much of anything for a long, long time."

I never saw the face, hidden beneath the ski mask, that night. I never learned his real name. I'm sure I wouldn't recognize his voice, since it was distorted by the howling wind. The heavy fur coat made it impossible to describe his build or weight—he could be fat or thin. All I know is his height—average, not tall and not short. So that's not much to go on.

He could be anywhere.

He could be anyone.

You could pass him as he walks alone, moving slowly along the boardwalk, feeding popcorn to the gulls while seated on a bench that usually faces the ocean. Or he might be the fellow eating a sandwich at a booth beside the window in a seashore diner. But there's a better chance he's the one parked with his feet dangling over the edge of a deserted dock or pier—usually at night—while the sea crashes against the pilings 20 feet below.

The Watcher

East Coast, U.S.A.

I recall seeing her from the time I had just finished the fourth grade in school. We were at the beach and she was sitting in the third-floor window of the old clapboard house, located at the south end of the beach, just beyond the end of the boardwalk. She was looking out toward the sea. We never called to her or did anything rotten, like throwing stones up at the building to get her attention. It was enough to just know she was there, that she was always there. Just rocking and watching, rocking and watching–as if she were waiting for someone. Even a young kid, like I was at the time, realized that there had to be a reason she never left the window.

Of course, we didn't know the entire story. We were happy to wonder if she ever left that spot. After all, she had to get up sometime, at least to eat or go to the bathroom, didn't she?

That seemed logical.

There wasn't a single time that we looked up at that green house and didn't see her. Rocking and watching. Rocking and watching. She just kept at it, over and over, for what seemed like forever.

Sometimes, while riding in the back seat of my parents' station wagon on the way back home from our two weeks at the beach, I wondered, just for a few minutes: Is she still up there, rocking away? Then the thought passed out of my mind and I didn't reflect on her for another year, until we were driving back to the beach at the start of our next summer vacation.

As soon as I placed my clothes in the dresser drawers of our cottage, I would run out onto the beach, head south, stop, turn around and look up. And there she would be, still rocking and watching–and still wearing that black high-collared dress with the white lace around her neck. Then–curiosity satisfied–I would dash off and officially begin my summer vacation.

It was years later–when I was 18 and had gotten a job and stayed at the beach the entire summer–that things changed drastically. She was there as usual when I arrived. But a month later the old lady at the window was the talk of the town. You see, "The Watcher" had died.

Now this was big news, and her obituary filled a complete page of the *Seashore Summer Weekly*. Word traveled fast and I, who never bothered to read a newspaper for all the time I had been away from home, grabbed a paper and eagerly read every word of the story under the headline and beside the picture of the empty rocking chair:

'The Watcher' passes on, an empty rocker near her window

One of the area's most colorful, but mysterious, characters died earlier this week. Gladys "The Watcher" Prim, 98, and widow of the late Captain Phillip Prim, who was lost at sea during World War I, died while rocking in her third floor window on Beach Lane.

Apparently, no one knew Mrs. Prim had passed on at her sentry post, and she remained in her wooden rocker for three days before someone alerted authorities that "The Watcher" was watching but had stopped rocking.

When asked, in a rare, exclusive interview six years ago, if she had any close friends, Mrs. Prim replied, "I'm 92 years old. Everyone I knew is dead and those I knew I didn't like anyway. So, no, I don't have a friend in the world. Besides, if you want some good advice, my dear, get rid of any so-called friends you may have. They are, or will become, nothing but trouble. My peculiar family members demand as much attention as I can handle, and I try to avoid them as much as is humanly possible."

At that time, the *Seashore Summer Weekly* reporter also was able to discover an answer to two of the area's most asked questions: Why does Mrs. Prim rock day and night in her window, and is she watching for anything in particular?

"A lot of people want to know why I'm here, in this chair," Mrs. Prim said. "Many claim I'm crazy. Well, they can think whatever they want. You see, I have enough age and money to do whatever I decide. But, since you asked, I will tell you this. I am not crazy at all. I have got this wonderful property with a very good view. Lived in this home for more than 70 years. I see everything that's going on in this little town from up here, and realize I am better off than most of the quite strange people along the beach and boardwalk.

"As to why I sit up here and rock. I enjoy it. Keeps me young. Also, I told my Phillip, when he went off to war in 1916, that I would wait for his ship to come back. That was very many years ago. But, as long as I keep watching, I truly believe there is still a chance he will be back. And the minute I give up and stop looking out for him, then that's the day that the hope is gone and he never will come home. Actually, young lady, it is up to me to keep the captain alive. So there is your answer."

Well, readers, our Watcher will watch no more, and with her passing also lost is any hope of the return of Captain Prim. Sadly, there is an empty chair in the window where Mrs. Gladys Prim used to sit and rock and watch, and our little beach town has lost a colorful and wonderful character.

Funeral services will be private. Her niece, Ms. Millicent Hester Prim, of Long Island, New York, who could not be reached for comment, survives Mrs. Prim.

The excitement associated with the death of Mrs. Prim passed rather quickly as I recall. But for weeks afterwards, many of us found ourselves looking up at the window, out of habit. But when we realized what we were doing, even before our eyes were able to focus on the third-floor window, we still stole a glance, hoping to see The Watcher rocking, as she had done for so long, at her post.

But that didn't happen, until later.

It was just a little more than a month after her official date of death that a young boy raced up the boardwalk, shouting hysterically, "SHE'S BACK! SHE'S BACK!"

When two people grabbed the boy and asked him to explain the commotion, he shouted, "THE WATCHER! SHE'S BACK!"

Not waiting for any further explanation, dozens of locals and visitors ran toward the beach area in front of the late Mrs. Prim's home and, like the youngster said, The Watcher was back—up in her favorite window staring out at the sea.

She was even rocking.

The confused crowd didn't know what to think, and with each passing minute the size of the mob rapidly increased in size. When two police officers arrived they saw the figure for themselves and rushed to the front porch. One was knocking on the glass, trying to attract the attention of anyone inside who might give an explanation, while the other paced the porch shaking his head in disbelief.

Within moments, an attractive young, blonde-haired woman appeared, spoke to the police. After a few moments the officers returned to the beach and addressed the crowd.

"We just spoke to Mrs. Prim's niece," the taller cop said. "It's a dummy, a store mannequin, she dressed up to look like The Watcher. That's it. Move along. Mystery's over. On your way, folks."

The explanation did not go over well with the crowd. I think a number of them were hoping the ghost of The Watcher had returned to her post. I know I was. Others were complaining that it was a stupid and mean trick to play, and certainly no way to honor the memory of the town icon.

Apparently, the young woman who had inherited Mrs. Prim's estate felt differently. In a newspaper article that appeared the following week, Millicent Hester Prim, the niece, said she had decided to erect a sort of museum attraction of her late aunt for the beach-going population. She explained that since the recently departed had become a legendary part of the lives of so many of the beach's guests and residents, the younger woman thought the rocking dummy would be an appropriate way to keep her relative's memory alive. The mannequin was dressed in Mrs. Prim's clothing, and a mechanical device moved the rocker, allowing the memorial Watcher to remain at her post 24 hours a day, seven days a week. And there she would stay.

Of course there was some debate.

One letter to the editor described the scenario as the small town's version of the Bates Motel in *Psycho*.

Another local town official said she was going to submit a law that no images of dead people could be placed in windows facing the beach, but that proposal died quietly.

Eventually, the uproar subsided, but some locals still questioned the sanity of the late Mrs. Prim's niece. Surprisingly, after about two weeks, a few complimentary letters appeared in the newspaper.

One in particular message stated, "Seeing our dear departed friend Mrs. Gladys Prim back at her post is both comfortable and comforting to me and others. Too many things in today's day and age change too quickly. The presence of The Watcher, our very own special symbol of the town, who was an innocent, even quirky, part of our life at the beach, makes me happy again. And, I must admit to all, I even wave to her, just as I used to, whenever I stroll beneath her lookout window. Thanks to the courage and creativity of Mrs. Prim's niece, our dear departed friend's memory will live on for all to see. Welcome home, Watcher. We're glad you're back to stay."

But all things planned do not go according to schedule, and the new Watcher proved to be not as dependable as the real McCoy. Oftentimes, the imi-

The old wharf steps rest directly below 'The Watcher's' window.

tation sentry would not be found at her appointed post. Hours would go by without a sighting of Mrs. Prim's replacement.

When that occurred, watchers of The Watcher began calling the Prim household, telling the new mistress to "get up there and put The Watcher back in her chair."

Those of us on the beach in front of the old green house would hear the phone ring off the hook, over and over and over again, each time The Watcher was off duty.

Eventually, "Watcher Watching" became a new beach sport, and the first one to spot an empty window would rush to the pay phone on the boardwalk—where the Prim household number was written boldly on the wall. The caller would proudly announce the absence of the late Mrs. Prim's double.

When The Watcher went missing, the calls never seemed to stop.

In small towns it's nearly impossible to keep a secret and, according to reliable sources, the decision to create the imitation Mrs. Gladys Prim was not the idea of the new young lady of the house, but the deceased's last demand.

In her will, as a condition of leaving her valuables, financial assets and home and property to her niece, The Watcher demanded that her rocker be occupied forever, in the form of a real person hired to take over the post or some other "appropriate representation."

Ms. Prim the Younger would own the home and do whatever she wanted with the money and other possessions, but the property could not be sold. And, The Watcher must remain at her post—apparently maintaining her lookout for Captain Prim, with the intent of keeping his memory alive. Of course, the arrangements were to remain a secret, and young Ms. Prim could not divulge the demands to anyone.

In exchange, all was hers. Naturally, the survivor agreed, but she had no way of knowing the ramifications that would occur both outside and inside The Watcher's home.

Large amounts of money have a way of making people immune to the unusual wants or bizarre opinions of others. But mannequins moving around under their own power in a locked room can have a way of unnerving the most stable individual.

Somehow, someway, the inanimate "Watcher II" was a bit more active than the original.

Things started to go wrong during the early morning hours, when normal people sleep and mannequins don't get up and go for a stroll. However, Mrs. Prim's double seemed to tire of rocking and watching. One night she left her post, somehow opened the door and fell down the steps, stopping on the second-floor landing in front of Millicent Hester Prim's bedroom door.

Thinking she was having a bad dream, the younger, living Prim carried the dummy back upstairs and placed her back into the rocker.

Two hours later, Watcher II was back, this time arriving with a thump against the door of the mistress of the home's bedchamber. When the younger woman pulled back on the knob, the dummy fell into the room and her painted blue eyes looked up, straight into the face of the new mistress of the house.

Determined to keep her inheritance and assert total dominance in her newly acquired residence, Millicent carried her aunt's double back to the third floor, dropped her into the rocker and raced down into the cellar. A few moments later she returned, with a long length of clothesline that she tied tightly around the mannequin's waist, securing the feisty creature to her motorized rocking chair.

That done, Millicent Hester Prim slammed the lookout room door and returned to her bedroom, located on the floor below.

All went well until noon the following day, when thumps and a crash were heard from the upstairs hall.

Rushing to investigate, Millicent discovered the dummy, dressed in its faded black dress, still tied to the chair, but resting facedown on the second-floor landing.

At this point, the younger woman was becoming increasingly fearful of what was occurring and how she would be able to live inside her house that was becoming progressively more "haunted."

In the days and weeks to come, trauma and tension increased to horrifying levels. Millicent Hester Prim locked the dummy in the lookout room, but it was still able to get out and fall down the stairs. Also, at irregular intervals, in the middle of the day and night, loud stamping of heavy feet was heard coming from the third-floor room—even though Watcher II was tied to the rocker.

The annoying telephone calls never stopped each time Watcher II decided to roam. Without being able to sleep or handle the unnerving disruptions throughout the day, Millicent Hester Prim was well on her way to becoming a classic basket case.

One day, while at the local food market, the younger Prim was overhead talking to the grocer. The older man had delivered food to her aunt's home each week while the older woman had been alive.

"I really shouldn't leave her too long," Millicent Hester Prim told the proprietor. "She has a tendency to fall out of her rocker quite often now. I must get back," and she asked the grocer to resume weekly food deliveries to her front porch.

Happy to do so, the grocer agreed, but he later told his wife that he was very confused during the conversation. He also mentioned that the younger Prim appeared to have aged 30 years in the few weeks since her kindly aunt's demise.

A week later, the grocer arrived at the Prim residence. Several days' worth of mail and newspapers were scattered on the porch deck. He rang the bell and knocked several times. When no one answered the door, he returned to his store and called the Prim home.

No one picked up the telephone. Fearing foul play, the grocer alerted the police.

When the officers heard nothing after ringing and knocking, they broke the front door glass, unlatched the lock and entered the building.

Slowly, they checked every room on the first two floors and found nothing.

Carefully, they climbed the dark, narrow stairway to the third floor. At the top step, a door–secured with a very large, clamped padlock–made it impossible for them to enter the lookout room. The sight of dozens of large, spikes that nailed the door and frame together was a bit unnerving and caught the officers' attention.

Leaning an ear to the door, one officer heard the rhythmic sound of rocking and also whispering. For a full minute the men banged on the thick wooden door, but no one responded to their cries. With the padlock and spikes securing the entryway from the hall, whoever might be in the room could not open the door from the other side.

Deciding that speed was important, one officer called for backup as the other shouted a warning that they were going to shoot off the lock, rip off the frame and enter with guns drawn.

Whoever was inside should drop to the floor and not move.

It took three shots to blow away the wood on the frame holding the metal hasp, but 15 minutes passed with both men shredding the door with axes. When the barrier started to give way, the taller cop kicked in what remained of the door. The two men, who since had been joined by four other officers, rushed inside not knowing what to expect.

Stopping abruptly, they stared at the macabre scene and then glanced at each other, seeking confirmation that they weren't hallucinating.

In the rocker near the window, wearing a black dress with a white lace collar, sat Millicent Hester Prim, rocking and mumbling incoherently. Strands of pasty drool fell from the corners of her mouth. A cheap white wig rested haphazardly atop her head. Large clumps of her blond hair were showing on either side.

Behind the rocking human vegetable, a nude mannequin was sprawled on the floor, its head facing toward the ceiling.

The young Mistress Prim's dazed head bobbed in rhythm to the motorized pace of the rocking chair. In the young woman's shaking hands was a crumpled copy of her deceased aunt's will. It was twisted and ripped on the edges. Ignoring the pistol-pointing officers, her glazed eyes stared at a strange site across the room.

Directly in front of the crazed niece, seated in a matching antique wooden rocker, was the decomposing corpse of Mrs. Gladys Prim, who seemed to be watching Watcher II, possibly to see if she performed her assigned task well.

The recently departed wore a matching black dress. But, with two months having passed since her Earth expiration date, Watcher I's brittle bones were beginning to make their way through a layer of paper thin, parchment-like skin.

The biggest surprise, however, was Mrs. and Ms. Prims' silent masculine companion, seated in a dark corner atop a padded, discolored wingchair.

It was impossible to identify the silent skeleton immediately, but the early 1900s-era naval uniform, complete with captain's cap balanced awkwardly atop the chalk-white skull, suggested it might be the remains of the long lost officer, who had been the object of The Watcher's attention for all those many long and lonely years.

Door to Nowhere

Fort Delaware, Pea Patch Island

I spend so much time at Fort Delaware that I think that every-one knows about the old, granite walled Civil War fort, locat-ed on Pea Patch Island in the center of the Delaware River, between the First State and nearby New Jersey.

But, for first-time readers of our books, it's best I give a little background about this popular, haunted historic site.

In the beginning

According to legend, several hundred years ago, a boat car-rying peas crashed against a submerged spit of land in the mid-dle of the Delaware River, just east of what is now the town of Delaware City. Soon the peas took root, sprouted and, eventual-ly, a body of land, known as Pea Patch Island formed and has grown to its present size.

In the late 1700s, Major Pierre L'Enfant, who designed the city of Washington, D.C., recommended that military fortifications be constructed on the island. It was during the War of 1812 that the first defenses were established and others were added in subsequent years. The current fort, in the shape of a large penta-gon, was completed in 1861. Constructed of brick and granite, the fortification was built to protect the growing cities along the Delaware River, particularly Philadelphia, Trenton and Wilmington from attacks by foreign powers.

The unknown strength of the Confederate Navy was a potential threat of major concern in the early days of the Civil War. Because of its strategic location in the center of the river, and with nearly 150 cannons, Fort Delaware was a formidable defense against any enemy ships that might attempt to pass within range of its guns.

When combined years later with artillery batteries at Fort Mott on the New Jersey shore and Fort DuPont on the Delaware coastline, the three forts provided excellent protection for the important shipping lanes leading to Philadelphia—and some degree of military presence was maintained in the region until the middle years of World War II.

But, no ships or enemy ever challenged the troops at Fort Delaware. Its cannons were never fired in anger and no significant battles were fought on the marshy soil of Pea Patch Island. However, nearly 150 years after the start of the War of Northern Aggression—or the War Between the States, as the Yankees call it—the island fortress stands as a symbol of Delaware's most tangible link to the Civil War.

And that connection is as a prison camp that hosted more than 33,000 Confederate soldiers.

Initially, no one thought of using Fort Delaware as an island penitentiary. But immediately after the Battle of Gettysburg in 1863, the War Department ordered 258 captured soldiers, most from the Commonwealth of Virginia, to Pea Patch Island. They were the first, but tens of thousands would follow, and nearly 2,500 would die of illness, battle wounds and disease.

Those Rebel soldiers are buried in a mass grave in the Finn's Point National Cemetery, a

A moat surrounds Fort Delaware. The main entrance is shown at right. A cannon stands on the ramparts.

79

short boat ride across the river in New Jersey. But, while the bodies of the dead are there, some believe their spirits still haunt Delaware's Civil War fortress.

Ghost/history tours

In the spring of 1997, Lee Jennings, Delaware state parks historian, was developing programs for Fort Delaware State Park. We had known each other for several years, and he asked if I would be interested in conducting a "haunted history tour."

Lee explained that he was familiar with walking tours at other historic sites—including Gettysburg, Williamsburg and Charleston—but they only used one guide who either told history or ghost stories. Our tour, he said, would be different, because there would be two guides. The historian would cover the facts and figures and historical content, and I would be the evening's "ghost host" and present folklore and legends. As an added plus, we would offer the events at night, by lantern light.

We were excited and thought we might get a *good* response.

We were wrong; we got a *great* response.

Our conservative schedule announced three tours that summer. They sold out so fast that we conducted 10. The following year, Friday night "Fort Delaware Ghost Tours" sold out 13 times. In 1999, we added October weekend Halloween events and a film crew spent three days on the island, filming and interviewing us about tales of Fort Delaware's ghosts. That October, *Ghost Waters* premiered on The Learning Channel, with our Civil War fort described in a segment as one of the six most haunted water sites in the United States.

So, are there ghosts at Fort Delaware? Do spirits roam Pea Patch Island? Have people seen apparitions?

The answers are Yes! Yes! and Yes!

In the summer of 2002, we will begin our sixth season of ghost tours at Fort Delaware. If this year is anything like the past five, we will come away with additional stories and tales of unexplained incidents to share with those who will visit the following year.

Plus, on or after nearly each ghost tour, we receive word of sightings, sounds or odd figures in photographs that visitors mail to the park office to be examined.

The list of ghost tales could fill half of this book. Some of the more frequently told tales are about the Man in the Black Cloak, the Man with the Lantern, the Disappearing Confederate Officer, the Vanishing Cook in the Haunted Kitchen, the Officer of the Day, who stands near the moat, the Ghost of General Archer, the Falling Portrait, the Phantom Cleaning Lady and the Headless Major.

While many stories about these sightings have been published in books in our *Spirits Between the Bays* series, the following is a new tale, learned during the 2001 ghost tour season that I'd like to share.

The Regulars

In the mid 1940s, the federal government closed its Fort Delaware installation. Until 1951 when the state created Fort Delaware State Park, the island fortress was abandoned. But it did not go unnoticed and unvisited.

Vandals, scavengers and thieves came onto the island and took everything not nailed down. Wooden doors, anything metal that might be of any scrap value, fireplace mantels, iron stoves, even a spiral staircase—all were carted off the island by thieves who figured they could put the unused goods to better use.

It's said that many a home in nearby Delaware City and the surrounding fishing villages and farmland are partially enhanced with former Fort Delaware furnishings.

Of course, most of the salvage operations occurred during darkness, and it was good if you had a boat. In fact, a trustworthy vessel was a requirement for those involved in this nocturnal pilfering.

One group of four guys was making so many expeditions to the island they were nicknamed, "The Regulars." While they tried to keep their activities quiet, word got out and they were approached by others who wanted to go along for the ride. One such pestering, annoyance was a cousin of one of The Regulars named Little Bobby.

He was a big boy, but only 15 years old. So he had a reputation for being awkward and clumsy. For several months, The Regulars kept him off their boat, but one weekday night the boy arrived at the dock ready to go.

After some serious discussion and heated debate, they agreed to take Little Bobby, as long as he did everything they said. Of course he agreed and off they went, out into the Delaware, heading for the east side of the island. There they docked their craft, covered it with brush and completed the short walk to the fort.

Once inside, the men split up. But Little Bobby was assigned to stick like glue to his cousin Nick.

For an hour, the youngster helped the other men carry their booty toward the shore so they could load it quickly into the boat. The one thing that Nick, and the others, told Little Bobby dozens of times was: "Don't go nywhere without looking. This place has secret passageways, trap doors that you could fall into and doors that go nowhere. Entire floors have been ripped up in some places. You could fall and get hurt or killed."

About two hours after their arrival, the group was completing its night's work. Nick, who was with Little Bobby on the second floor, in the building on the east, Jersey, side of the Parade Ground, told the kid he was going to go check on their departure time. When Little Bobby gave no response, Nick didn't push for a reply and walked down the steps.

Two minutes latter, Little Bobby was smiling with delight as he held up a hand-carved mantle that at one time had probably graced the fireplace of a general. The ornate plank was heavy, but he was strong and lifted it over his head and rested it on his right shoulder.

Looking around, he didn't see cousin Nick. Suddenly, he began getting a little scared in the dark room. After all, it was an abandoned fort that everyone in three states knew was haunted, plus it was pitch black and he was alone.

Running to a window that overlooked the Parade Ground, he saw Nick running fast toward the Sallyport, the entrance near the Moat. Apparently, Little Bobby thought he was being left behind. Panicked, he tried to pry open the window with one hand. No way was he going to put down his prize mantle. But the sash wouldn't open. It had been nailed shut. Looking around quickly in the dark, he couldn't find the stairway or entrance they had used. Then suddenly, about 12 feet to his left, on the outside wall was a white door. It would lead directly to a quick route to the Parade Ground, Little Bobby thought.

He rushed toward the door, yanked back on the knob and ran onto an invisible layer of thin air.

The door went nowhere.

The floor or stairs, or whatever had been there years ago, was gone. Little Bobby, with his mantel in tow, fell against the jagged granite walkway 20 feet below.

The Regulars turned when they heard the crash. Lines of light from their flashlights shone like ray gun beams, crisscrossing rapidly as they moved from side to side, up and down.

Then Nick saw the open door and raced to the mound lying underneath. Little Bobby was dead. The thin edge of his souvenir mantel had crushed the boys' throat in the fall.

Panic had to be controlled and, in surprisingly little time, The Regulars had developed a plan that involved not reporting Little Bobby's death on Pea Patch, but delivering the corpse to the mainland with a believable story.

After they loaded the boat with their haul, which included Little Bobby's prize mantel, they tied a rope around the dead boy and dragged him back to shore, hoping the water would fill up in his lungs. To anyone not looking for foul play, it would appear that the teenager had drowned.

To The Regulars' relief, their plan worked and Little Bobby was laid to rest, the spoils were divided and the ornate mantel ended up—through barter or as a gift or through an antique sale—above a fireplace in a restored Victorian home in the city's historic district.

The day after the mantle was installed, however, the homeowner began to notice small puddles of water at the side of the hearth, below the fireplace. Thinking it might be a leak

The edge of the 'door to nowhere' can be seen on the upper level of the second arch from the right.

from the chimney, the homeowners called in an expert and no cracks or flaws were found in the structure.

A few days later, more moisture. Then, a week later, even a larger pool of water. It was as if the size of the puddle was increasing, no matter how often they mopped up the water,

Perhaps the strangest part of the tale was that the water arrived during a period of serious drought, so there was no way that rain could be the cause.

The last straw came when the wife came down for breakfast one weekday and found a stream of water running down the wall and flowing across the floor. The town water department inspector saw it, shook his head and could offer no coherent explanation. Joking, he said, that maybe there was a ghost in the house.

Rather than relax the frustrated couple, the remark only intensified their effort to get to the source of the problem. Through a mutual friend of a friend of a friend, they were introduced to a psychic—who stressed that she did not want to know anything about their specific paranormal problem before visiting their troubled home.

One Sunday afternoon, the older lady, dressed in black, arrived unannounced. After a brief introduction, she walked from room to room, passed right through the kitchen where the trouble had occurred and headed for a pantry in the rear of the first floor. Then, the lady in black suddenly returned and stopped in front of the fireplace, closed her eyes and grabbed the mantel with both hands.

"It needs to leave," she said, speaking to no one in particular. "Take this back where it belongs and your troubles will end." Then she turned and walked out the front door, without answering any of the half-dozen questions the couple shouted in her direction. But, at least they now had a clue, a strange clue, but a clue nonetheless.

After a call to a neighbor, who had done some historic preservation work, they determined that the mantel probably had been taken from Fort Delaware. That night, they removed the ornate woodwork, walked to the fort office and left the carved wooden slab leaning against the front door.

There's no way to tell whether it was the same mantle that crushed Little Bobby's neck. Maybe? Probably? It would make sense if it was, but no one will ever know for sure.

At least the mantelpiece is back where it belongs. But one park official, who didn't want his name used, said the carpenters tried to mount it several times, and it would not stay put. He told me it's now in storage, with several other suspected haunted objects, in a secret room in the fort that visitors are not able to access and that the help doesn't want to go near.

But the dripping has stopped in the Victorian home. And now that Fort Delaware State Park is under constant use and continual reconstruction, the scavengers are long gone.

But the ghosts?

Oh, the ghosts. They never leave. In fact, we seem to get more of them each year.

Maybe that's because Fort Delaware is so much like it was 150 years ago, and because the island is so isolated--with no cars or electricity or modern intrusions—that the spirits feel very comfortable there.

In the movie *Field of Dreams*, they say: "Build it and they will come."

At Fort Delaware, we say: "Keep it exactly as it was, and they will come back."

Author's note: Fort Delaware State Park is open to the public from April through October. It is located on Pea Patch Island and reached by a short ferry ride. The vessel leaves the Delaware City, Del., dock on Clinton Street at regular intervals. Call the park office at (302) 834-7941 for information on park hours, special events, the living history program, Garrison Weekend and the Ghost/Lantern Tours.

The ghost tours are usually presented on selected Friday evenings from June through September. There are special Halloween tours during weekends in October.

Space is limited and reservations are suggested for this popular guided evening programs. Please tell park personnel that you heard about the fort through our books. We will appreciate it. Autographed copies of Ed's books are sold in the Fort Delaware Civil War Shop.

Spirits Abound
Around Elk Landing

Elkton, Maryland

I t's amazing where ghost leads come from. Many originate
during phone calls, through letters and as a result of comments made during a book signing or storytelling program.
But this recommendation was rather unusual, coming not from
an anonymous source, or from someone in the ghost hunting
business. No, the spark that directed me along the trail of the
ghosts near Landing Lane was a young schoolteacher—and she
first heard about the phantoms from her young students.

For years I have received reports of apparitions and restless
souls in the vicinity of the confluence of the Big and Little Elk
creeks. As usual, I dropped the unassociated stories and clues in a
folder awaiting my attention. Following a "reading day" promotion
in a Cecil County, Maryland, school, a history teacher approached
me, slipped a card with her number on it into my hand, and said,
"I have got stories for you. Please give me a call."

Two days later, during a phone conversation, she told me
that several of her students who live near Historic Elk Landing,
off Route 40 at the west end of Elkton, reported unexplained,
ghostly sightings in their neighborhood. A week later, over coffee at a diner at the edge of town, the teacher, who demanded
that I not mention her name or the name of her school, presented me with a set of notes that summarized her students' ghostly
accounts.

Since I had a very good friend in the history business, and he happened to be president of the Historic Elk Landing site, I contacted Mike Dixon.

You must understand, Mike Dixon is a serious historian, who really knows his stuff. Toss Mike a date and you'll get a response that will let you know who of importance died on that date, what significant historical event occurred on or near that date and, his specialty, why that particular date is significant in the annuls of recorded Cecil County, Maryland, history.

Mike is an official of the Historical Society of Cecil County. He's also associated with a dozen other similar groups in Maryland and Delaware, and gets several phone calls each week from individuals seeking information about historical topics.

He and I work together throughout the year offering workshops, cemetery tours and fundraising programs that instruct others about the irrefutable connection between history and folklore—or as I like to describe it: "History and haunts—you can't have one without the other."

Over the years we've learned from each other. During joint programs, I jibe with him, mentioning, "Mike, our preeminent historian, will tend to let facts get in the way of a good story."

To which he responds in good humor, "And, of course, Ed never lets facts enter into any of his tall tales and stories."

Mike also doesn't believe in ghosts. Of course, I do.

This also is a bone of contention, but it became a matter of significant interest to us both when specters were reported in the vicinity and on the grounds of Historic Elk Landing.

You see, Mike is not only the president, but

The old plantation house at Historic Elk Landing, overlooking the nearby river

one of the founders of the Historic Elk Landing Foundation. The thought of nameless spirits roaming the hallways of the old, white, three-story mansion, plus phantoms flitting in and out of the old stone structure on the banks of the Big Elk Creek and ghosts gathering near the shore of the waterway where the British force invaded in 1813 is something serious scholars don't want to know about and tend not to acknowledge even when told.

To be honest, many historical types can't process paranormal-related information. Their minds don't function that way. It's as if someone began talking in Martian to you at a cash register line in WalMart. Reports of ghosts are alien to any self-respecting historian's sense of "research" and such hearsay sullies up their efforts to collect "verifiable data."

Paranormal reports offered by living human beings are not satisfactory. Any true historian must secure his proof about almost anything in a written document made by some unknown, unseen entity that has been dead 200 years. This sends them into the bowels of musty rooms where they read old newspapers, looking for exciting things—like the date that someone purchased a plot of land or when a person died and, finally, the quest that really gets their juices charged up: Who might be related to whom.

Also, historical fact hunting is a dangerous occupation. After long years of conducting this kind of fun work, there are reports of some historians going blind from reading swirling script and fine print with strange lettering. Others, it's been said, have contracted unusual diseases after breathing infectious, 18th-century mold spores that are lurking in old, smelly books, just waiting for an unsuspecting historian to crack them open.

But, that said, let's get back to the subject of ghosts along the Big Elk Creek.

Mike—who more than once reminds me he has not yet met a ghost, and therefore is sure that they don't exist—knew I had been toying with the idea of writing up reports of paranormal events in and around Historic Elk Landing. Since the ghost stories and evening Ghost Lantern Tours at Fort Delaware State Park had helped gain the site national attention, Mike suggested that I might want to include the Hollingsworth House sightings and tales in one of my books.

Of course, I didn't need much urging, and the stories I have heard from a number of sources are unusual enough to merit sharing. Also, as in the case of 90 percent of the paranormal reports I have received, these are related to a significant historic site that is in the process of being preserved for future generations.

History

Historic Elk Landing is described as a nearly "forgotten port at the head of the Chesapeake Bay." During America's late Colonial and early Federal periods (1770 to 1820), Elk Landing was the mid-Atlantic's northernmost navigable inland waterway. Over time, it became a preferred north-and-south travel route for many well-known patriots.

The site's brochure claims that George Washington, Thomas Jefferson and Lafayette, as well as other notable personages passed through the area on their way to Philadelphia, the country's first Capitol.

This seems possible since road travel was horrible and America's waterways offered a smoother ride and, in some cases, faster and more reliable service.

The area at the west end of present day Elkton also served as a shipping and supply port for America's Continental Army during the Revolution. In August 1777, 16,000 British soldiers and Hessians passed south of Elk Landing on their way toward Philadelphia and the Battle of the Brandywine, which occurred in September near Chadd's Ford, Pennsylvania.

A few decades later, during the War of 1812, Fort Hollingsworth, located at Elk Landing—along with nearby Fort Defiance—defended Elkton from burning by British invaders, who returned to the area in April 1813.

My friend Mike also proudly pointed out that this same group of British invaders, under the command of Admiral Cockburn, later marched into Washington, D.C., and sacked and burned the White House.

A bit smugly, the Cecil County historian added, "That force met their match when they tried the same thing here in Elkton. We sent them packing,"

I told Mike I would be sure to get that statement into the chapter.

Now, back to Elk Landing's history.

In the early 19th century, Elk Landing served as a port, harboring boats loaded with flour, iron, nails, wood, pork and lumber that headed for Baltimore and returned with coal, molasses, coffee and whiskey.

In the late 1880s, Henry Deibert constructed canal boats at Elk Landing. The craft were launched sideways into the Little Elk Creek. The old stone building that still stands near the water was originally constructed as a dwelling and later became a tavern.

Some fascinating information linked to the causes of ghostly reports in the area may have their origin centuries before the arrival of European settlers. The land, originally owned by the Hollingsworth family of Cecil County is an historic tract and located at the confluence of the Little Elk and Big Elk creeks.

While this location played a major role in Colonial transportation and commerce, American Indians also valued its natural beauty and strategic importance. For centuries, they used the meeting point of the two rivers as a trading post and village.

In the 1980s, the Cecil County Detention facility, located adjacent to Historic Elk Landing's grounds, was under construction. During excavation, several American Indian graves were unearthed. Archaeologists, including Cecil County historian and archaeological expert George Reynolds, were called in to verify the remains' authenticity and age.

Members of Reynold's Northeast Chapter of the Archaeological Society of Maryland plus staff of Mid-Atlantic Archaeological Research conducted excavations on the 13-acre detention site. They uncovered hundreds of pieces of Indian pottery, more than 100 arrowheads and, about four feet below the surface, found a skeleton in a grave.

The human bones were sent to the Smithsonian Institution, which returned a report dating the remains at about 1,400 A.D. Later more Indian gravesites were found.

The investigation concluded that the small peninsula had been a large Indian village and burial ground many years before the white settlers recognized its geographic importance and built their settlement there.

During the course of the detention facility's construction, workmen reported unusual sightings and spoke of unexplained sounds and events. Staff and prisoners reported paranormal activity even after the jail opened in 1984. (See *Opening the Door*, Vol. II of the *Spirits Between the Bays* series.)

With such a varied and rich history—involving American Indians, British invaders, American defenders, Colonial settlers, shipbuilders, traders, tavern patrons and, even the possibility of a yet undiscovered slave gravesite—it seems logical that Historic Elk Landing might be a haven for restless spirits that continue to roam.

Haunts

Mike took me to Elk Landing soon after the foundation was established. Proud of his new creation, he asked me what I thought. Immediately, I said, "Mike, this place has got to be haunted. Of course, if it is, it will be a boost to your tourism trade."

Of course, I knew his reply, which went something like, "Ed, have you ever been to a place that wasn't haunted?"

"Your house," I said, laughing. Then we roamed the property, complete with work sheds, a river walk area, old plantation home and a stone building that looked like it was ready to fall over but which would be a perfect site for a séance or ghost hunting investigation.

Somehow, unknown to me or Mike, a number of ghost hunters discovered the site and called me with reports of "serious activity" in the main house and in the area along the river and stone building.

One woman told me, "I was at the

The old stone house at the river's edge is a ghost hunter's dream home.

Hollingsworth House during an open event they held there. I became so overwhelmed with grief, and the surroundings became so hot and frightening, that I had to leave my friends and run from the building. I found solace near the old stone house beside the water. But I would never, ever go back into that haunted house again."

I told her that I found her comments interesting, particularly because the place doesn't give me the creeps at all. But I'm not a good one to make judgments about the ghostly presence in historic sites. Maybe I've been in so many reported haunted places that I'm immune to paranormal vibes. I never claimed I "had the gift" and I really don't want it. All I look for are the stories.

And the stories about horrifying feelings in Hollingsworth House kept coming, even though I wasn't seeking them.

In the mail I received a photograph containing a vortex–a streak of bright light that appears in developed pictures. It is not seen at the time the picture is taken, but noticed later, when the developed pictures are picked up after processing. In this photo, a distinct line of white can be seen flying across one of the first-floor rooms of the Hollingsworth plantation house at Elk Landing.

"I had several people, who are experts in the area of paranormal photography, look at it," the owner told me. "And they confirmed it is a vortex."

The bright line (vortex) and the more commonly captured "orbs," small round dots that appear to be floating, are believed to indicate the presence of spirit energy.

One night, after my friend Jackie LaGuardia McCabe and I completed a "Folksongs and Folktales" program for families on a beautiful summer evening, an older lady approached me. She knew I wrote ghost stories and asked, "Have you recorded the ghosts in this house yet?" pointing to the main building that was undergoing restoration.

"Not really," I said.

"Well, it's infested," she replied. "The last time I felt this much activity was during my visit to Buckingham Palace and the Tower of London. I've felt Indian spirits, military men, and travelers. Many in pain and others just passing through. I tried my best to help some pass to the other side, but I don't have enough time, and it looks like they are closing things up. But please tell those in charge. They should get a shaman or psychic out here. It needs a lot of cleansing."

Naturally, I relayed the message to Mike and he told me they were repairing the place.

I explained to him that the cleansing the lady suggested had to do with spiritual ceremony, not reconstruction, but he didn't want to hear it. But, before he walked off to lock the gate, I told him that paranormal activity increased dramatically when an old site was being rebuilt. The loud noises and ripping out of walls and construction activity seems to stir the ghosts up. I stressed that I had gotten that same report over and over and over from people who owned or worked in historic sites throughout the region.

Mike rolled his eyes and waved me off, saying, "Well, then we'll have ghosts here for the next 20 years, because it will be that long before everything is done."

Smiling, I said, "Then that will be good for business," and walked away.

Earlier that evening, while preparing for the concert with Jackie, two tour guides at the house approached me and mentioned that they had seen fast-moving apparitions and felt the presence of someone behind them when they were inside the old structure.

"It's just so cold all of a sudden," one lady said. "It's as if someone is watching you."

Looking at the old portraits—of long dead people who had lived in the house—that hang in the first floor of the plantation house would give anyone the willies. I guess sitting in one position for such a long time gives them a reason to look miserable but if you stare at them long enough they become downright frightening.

One painting is charred with a black tint, giving evidence of a fire that nearly destroyed the plantation house structure many years ago. Some visitors, who have gotten the chills or eerie feelings of an invisible presence while walking through the building, have suggested that there may have been deaths in the fire. But there is no documentation of that having occurred.

A young man suggested that a slave ship may have crashed in the Big Elk Creek and those chained to their seats and oars drowned in shallow water within sight of shore. This is the stuff of which major league legends are made, but even I, with my fertile imagination, have not heard any other person confirm or suggest that event may be true.

From the mouths of babes

Another tale, with more a more verifiable foundation, involves a young militiaman who was killed when ammunition stored on the site exploded. His distressed bride, in a long white gown, is said to float along the creek bank, lamenting his tragic loss and awaiting his return.

My unnamed schoolteacher, however, delivered the most interesting stories. She said she had known about the ghosts at the Cecil County jail and was about to mention that usual story to her class when she was presenting the unit on the War of 1812. She also had planned to tell her students about the British invasion at Elk Landing in 1813 and Admiral Cockburn's torching of Havre de Grace, Georgetown and the White House, plus the legend of the Kitty Knight House.

Before she could get into the chapter, one student raised his hand and asked her if she knew about the soldier ghosts that roamed the street and fields off Landing Lane.

"I was shocked," said Margie (we'll give my teacher friend the name Margie for the purposes of identification in this story). "I hadn't mentioned the word ghost and this boy brought up the subject. He said he has seen soldiers with muskets walking down Landing Lane, toward Elk Landing, and they pass right through the metal gate and keep going toward the creek and disappear."

I told her I was amazed and excited by her story.

She said, "That's nothing. When I asked him, 'You mean you've actually seen soldiers?' he matter-of-factly replied. 'I've talked to them, and to the ladies, too.' He said he's sat near the creek and watched the soldiers and the women cooking food in old black pots that were hanging over a fire. He described the pot being suspended by three short pieces of metal. There is no way that particular student, who rarely says a word in my class, would go into that much detail. His comments include information that he could not have known before. But I was quite pleased with his interest in sharing these comments.

"He told me that after looking at them a while, the ghosts would just vanish, right before his eyes, all at the same time.

"Then another student said he lives in Hollingsworth Manor and he and his friends—and even his parents—can smell smoke at night, like the kind coming from campfires. Other times they hear gunshots during the night, and they can look out their upstairs windows toward the historic property, but there is nothing there to see."

I told her that re-enactors, like the Cecil County Militia, sometimes dress up in uniform and perform at Elk Landing for special events. But she cut me off and replied, "During the work week and at 3 o'clock in the morning?"

I shrugged my shoulders.

"I'm not trying to argue with you," she said. "All I wanted to do is share what they told me. I find their comments interesting. You don't seem to be impressed, telling me about the re-enactors. I know people do that at places like Elk Landing. But these events, happening during the week, seem a little unusual to me. Don't you agree?" she asked.

Nodding my head, I assured her that the theory made sense. Apparently satisfied that I had taken her and her students' comments seriously, she thanked me for my time and began to leave.

I asked her to wait. Then, I pulled out a manila folder and passed it toward her across the top of the table.

As she opened the file, I explained that I get a lot of reports from different sources about scores of different sites, whether they be homes or museums or historic locations. When that happens, I immediately place the information in an ever-growing set of files. They remain there until I have enough material for a story, or until what I had heard is verified, or at least confirmed, by another source.

Inside the file folder was a child's drawing of an Indian, with a single feather in his headband, facing what looked like a soldier, dressed in an old-fashioned uniform. The two figures appeared to be talking to each other, perhaps trading or trying to communicate.

I explained that more than three years ago, after a presentation at a library in Delaware, a lady and her daughter came up to me and asked if I had ever heard of Elk Landing.

At that time I had no idea that an historic site even existed beside the county jail. I did know about the Indian burial ground, but not the War of 1812 connection. I listened, took the information and kept the picture and interview notes in the folder. When Mike Dixon's group began working at the site, it reminded me to find the information

Reaching across the diner table, I also showed Margie the notes that I had taken during that meeting. On lined paper my writing stated, "Girl's mother said in afternoon, about sunset, walking beside Big Elk Creek at the end of Landing Lane, they heard gunshots and smelled smoke from campfire."

My teacher guest put down the drawing and notes and passed them back.

"That's very helpful, " she said, "Do you mind if I share this with my kids, tell them I talked to you?"

I assured her that would be fine. In fact, I promised to send a few books to her about area history and legends that the students might find interesting.

As she got up to leave, she paused, stood at the edge of the table, looked down on me and said, "I'm a believer. So you don't have to convince me that something is down there, along the creek or in that old house. It's a creepy looking place. But I'm just amazed that these kids, several of them, shared these stories with me so easily. They sound authentic to me, but I'm not an expert. Their comments were spontaneous, I mean, it wasn't part of an assignment that I might have told them to do for extra credit or homework. I just gave the title of the next unit and they began talking about ghosts they had seen, or someone close to them has seen, in that area. I didn't encourage them, but once they started talking, I didn't make them stop, either."

Author's note: Historic Elk Landing is the peninsula of land between the Big Elk Creek and the Little Elk Creek, located on Landing Lane just off Route 40, in Elkton, Md. Events are held throughout the year. For information, call (410) 620-6400 or send e-mail to [info@elklanding.org] or visit the web site at [www.elklanding.org].

Late for His Own Funeral

Eastern Shore of Maryland

I love old post offices, the kind that are tucked away in the corner of a small town general store, or the ones that look like they're housed in an old converted garage that needs a good coat of paint. They have their own special smell, they're welcoming and they make people want to go inside and even chat and congregate a spell.

But if you want to experience a special moment inside their doors, you better move along quickly. You see, they're disappearing fast, being replaced by modern, 21st-century architecture that's cold, impersonal, functional, and, of course, the bureaucrat officials will tell you, supposed to give the impression that the brand new, ugly-as-sin building really has that "old-fashioned" charm.

The big-thinking decision makers and college-educated federal building designers—who all happen to live, work and goof off in their spare time in big cities like Washington and Philly and New York, and who have never been to a fishing village, farm town or county seat—let you know that they have all the answers to what a replacement post office should look like.

But they'll tell you that their main goal is transformation of the outdated sites into new ones that are "user-friendly" (make that high-tech and ugly) and "centrally located" (that means out of the center of town and in a new, sterile strip mall that has no other tenants).

The all look alike—metal wrapped, perfectly square warehouses with as few windows as possible. For an added "personal touch" to blend into any surrounding, the architect will add something that's supposed to look like a bell tower (made out of lime green or dull beige aluminum siding). Some places will go rustic and toss up a section or two of made-in-China, synthetic split rail fencing at the entrance (that really just blocks your way to the door).

Others will be decorated with what some "authority" had told them are "old time" colors. Have you ever seen what Williamsburg blue and Colonial buff look like on sheets of aluminum extending 40 feet in length and width and 25 feet high?

So, the best thing to do if you've gotta go and use one of these, cold, impersonal, cookie-cutter-style, modern postal administrative centers with no hint of local character is: Run in very early in the morning and get out as fast as you can—or toss your mail into the outside blue box and keep on driving.

But this rambling tangent has nothing to do with the essence of our ghost story, except to lead into the fact that the old, one-room, ramshackle post office where this story took place is no longer there. It, too, is long gone as they say, replaced down the road with one of them bell-tower jobs, and it's even got an old anchor in front, painted bright blue, resting on the patch of grass to the side of the entrance and near the American flag.

At least they haven't worked on modernizing and sanitizing the appearance of Old Glory—not yet anyway, but give them time.

Well, it was two years ago, after a library program in one of the southern counties on the Eastern Shore of Maryland, south of Salisbury, that a lady approached me and said, "I got a good one for you. If you want it."

"I said, 'Sure, I always need more material.' "

She explained that she was postmistress of a small office in the next town. It was late on a Saturday afternoon, and I agreed to follow her to the old postal building. She wanted to show me where the "very unusual events" had happened. "And," she said, "you just have to see my post office. It's the cutest little place. So nice and homey, and I got a wonderful view of the water."

We arrived about 5 o'clock, as it was getting dark. Polly, the postmistress, gave me a tour (it didn't take long) and pointed out the window to the wide expanse of the picturesque, tree-lined river that ran through town on its way to the Chesapeake Bay. In the distance, the sun was setting in the west, gulls were squawking as they circled overhead and landed on the nearby pier. Like a steady beat of a fine pocket watch, gentle waves could be heard lapping at the shoreline.

I leaned back in a rocker as Polly put on some water for tea, turned on a soft lamp (not a florescent overhead). Then she began.

"I been here 12 years," she said, leaning forward and smiling as she talked. She was in her 30s, had two little girls, said she liked working close to home and was lucky to have enough seniority to get her weekends off.

"Things started to change in the last five years," she said. "People started getting cremated more, and they'd come through here."

The fact that things were changing wasn't anything new, so I let that comment pass. But the word "cremated" caught my attention and caused me to ask her to go back to the beginning and explain what she was talking about.

Regrouping, and after responding to some questions I provided, Polly's story became more clear.

With society's acceptance and the dramatic increase in cremations, urns filled with ashes of the deceased are being shipped through the mail much more frequently today than even one or two years ago. Many times, she said, the remains of relatives living far away are mailed—in a box containing a metal or ceramic urn—directly to the home of the deceased's survivors. But, Polly said, a fair number of dead people are mailed to funeral homes around the country for a scheduled service.

"If the person doesn't get here on time," Polly said, "that can really put a crimp in the service. Today," she said, adding a smile, "you can really be late for your own funeral."

One year before, Polly was working the window on a Friday afternoon. It was just past the daily rush period, and a woman approached her asking for a package. It had been sent to the post office and was to be held for pickup.

Polly took the printed slip, went into the back room of the small building to locate the package. About 15 minutes passed, and she was still looking, when the counter bell began ringing repeatedly.

"I came back out and the lady began shouting at me, demanding that I turn over her parcel. She shouted that she was going to be late for a memorial service. Well, I wasn't used to being shouted at, and I told her I couldn't find her package. Then she starts waving her hands up in the air, and pacing and yelling and going on and on and on. Finally, I got her to calm down and explain the problem.

"The story was," Polly told me, "she had been sent to pick up the 'remains' of Uncle Wilbur, who had died in Michigan two weeks earlier. His funeral service was going to take place at the town graveyard in less than an hour. That's when they were going to officially bury his ashes.

"She was beside herself, because the hole was dug and all the locals and out-of-towners were already at the funeral parlor. Soon they would be heading over to the grave. She said her boyfriend was out in my parking lot with the car running, ready to deliver her and Uncle Wilber to the burial plot."

"What happened next?" I asked.

Polly explained that she was about to make a few calls to other post offices nearby, in case Uncle Wilber had been dropped off at the wrong building. But, the woman realized that even if the dead uncle could be located he wouldn't make it to town in time for his funeral.

"She told me to get her a box, an official postal box, the biggest one I could find. She said she wanted one with red, white and blue all over it, and that I should get it ready to seal. Then she ran outside and came back in carrying a huge stone. She took it off of our walkway. Now that wasn't right, but I wasn't about to argue with her. She had bigger problems than being charged with stealing federal property, and I decided to let her go on that. Besides, I could replace the rock easier than she could find her dead uncle.

"She slammed the rock on the counter and told me to put it in the box, then seal it up with 'priority' tape, put a lot of postage on the top of the container. I cancelled the postage meter with my date stamper for her to make it look more realistic. She said that she would pay me whatever it cost.

"I knew what she was doing before she told me. She said she was going to drive up to the cemetery with the box and have the undertaker put it in the grave. I asked what would happen if they wanted to open it up and pull out the urn, but she said she'd make a scene and tell them she couldn't bear to look inside. 'Leave that to me! It's not your damn problem!' she told me, real impolite. So, I just sold her the empty box and stamps and off she went with my rock."

Polly said the lady promised to return in a week and pick up the real Uncle Wilbur and she told the postmistress not to give him away to anyone else that might come looking.

"Then," Polly said, "the woman laughed, and said, 'Like who's going to come in and ask for him, what with him already in the ground.' In a flash she went off, hopped in the boyfriend's car and I never saw her again. She never came back for the real package. But Uncle Wilber arrived the following Tuesday. I knew it was him, because I remembered the name of the lady and the commotion and the information on the claim slip she gave me the previous Friday. No way I would forget that scene."

I waited, giving Polly a few moments to regroup. Then I listened as she continued with her story.

"Uncle Wilber sat in the back for a few weeks, not bothering a soul," Polly said. "But we don't have much shelf space, and I was getting annoyed after about a month, since I knew nobody was gonna come and get him. But there was another problem, I got an older lady, named Justine, who comes in on Saturdays and when I need help during the week. She's a part timer, nice thing, but she's into superstitions and tarot and astrology and all that hocus-pocus." Then suddenly, Polly looked at me with a concerned look and said, "No offense toward you and what you do, I hope you understand."

I smiled. "Relax," I told her, "I hear it all the time. Keep going. This is getting really good."

Apparently, Justine began hearing tapping noises coming from the storage shelves in the room just behind the counter. Polly said the steady tapping only seemed to occur when Justine was working in the front of the building and the rhythmic noises stopped the moment she entered the back room.

The annoyance had been going on for about a month before Justine alerted her boss.

"I thought she was crazy, what with all that mumbo jumbo she was into," Polly said. "I told her it was the wind. I also lied and told her I had heard it too, but it was just the tapping of the tree limbs against the building when the wind blew too hard. That seemed to keep her happy for a few more weeks, but then there was a bigger problem.

"One Saturday, a customer was out at the counter and asked Justine why she was playing the radio so loud," Polly said. "She told her the tapping in the back room was driving her crazy, and the lady said, 'Yeah. I heard it last week when I was in here. If I had to deal with that all day long I'd go crazy, too. Where's it coming from?'

"Justine was so happy to have someone else hear it, that she started to clap her hands and reached across the counter to shake the woman's hand. At that moment, they both heard a crashing sound that seemed to come from the back room. The two of them raced to the doorway to look and they saw a box in the middle of the doorway. Not at the base of the shelf where it had been resting, but 15 feet away from the shelving. There was no way it could have fallen there. It had to fly through the air or be picked up and dropped there."

Polly said the customer ran out of the post office, leaving her change and stamps on the counter. Justine called Polly at her home and the postmistress drove into town to speak with Justine and examine the box.

Together, they pushed the box into the back room and opened it very carefully. Inside was the urn, apparently containing the ashes of Uncle Wilbur.

"Of course," Polly said, "Justine was frantic with fright. She said she was going to bring in blessed candles and incense and wear a special charm to ward off the evil spirits. She asked if I wanted one, too. When I declined she seemed a little insulted, but I was too busy trying to think of what to do with our deceased in a box to care about Justine's feelings."

After her helper left, Polly said she resealed the parcel and moved it into an outside storage shed where unclaimed items were stored until the annual postal auction or someone arrived to make a claim.

Unfortunately, the tapping didn't stop. In fact, it increased.

"It was so loud I could hear it from inside this building while I was working. Now it would occur in the morning, in the afternoon, you name it," Polly said. "There was no systematic time or any reason for it to happen. Good weather or bad, rain or snow, wind or calm seas. I was going crazy. Plus, it was louder than before. If I told my regional manager, then he would think I was totally nuts. When I couldn't keep it to myself any longer—and I wasn't going to get involved with Justine and any of her crazy mumbo jumbo, believe me—I decided to go to Henry."

"Henry?" I wondered who this guy was and how he was going to fit into the progression of crazy events.

"Right, Henry," Polly said, smiling. "He's a regular, retired and a fascinating man. A lot of people don't understand Henry because he's into so many different things—UFOs, archeology, magnetic fields, crop circles and history. If I was to describe Henry, I'd say he has the correct balance between the paranormal and science. He's been a speaker at conventions around the country, knows a lot of famous people. You should see the mail he gets, from Washington, California, just about everywhere. He's our resident expert on just about everything, and the nicest man. When he comes into the post office and begins to chatter, no one wants to leave the place. Gets so crowded in here I can't tell the customers from the hangers on, and I have to shoo them all out, and off they go following Henry toward the dock like he's the Pied Piper."

After explaining the situation to Henry, he and Polly decided the deceased had to be put to rest. They went to the town cemetery late one evening and sprinkled Uncle Wilber's ashes onto of his gravesite. That was Henry's best recommendation to solve the problem.

"I wasn't ever in a graveyard at night," Polly said, "but Henry's spent a lot of time in cemeteries all over the country, doing research. So while I was uneasy, I wasn't afraid. He was very helpful, didn't look at me like I was crazy when I told him my problem. Seemed like he was real interested in listening and helping me. Like you are doing now. In fact, I'd say Henry's a lot like you, only older," Polly said, laughing.

"After that night, all the banging and annoyances stopped," Polly said she was relieved. "It was all over, just like that. Justine and me, we never talked about it again. Like I expected, nobody ever came back to claim Uncle Wilber, so if Henry and me didn't let him out and sprinkle him on his mound up there, I believe he would still be very upset and calling out for help. That's what it was, you know. Trying to get us to do the right thing, and I think we did."

I thanked Polly for a wonderful story, and started to get up from my chair. I thought the tale was over, but there was one more part of the yarn that she said I had to hear.

"I thought that was it, too," Polly said. "But three weeks later Henry came in with a folder filled with a photocopy of an obituary from Michigan. He flew in here like a little whirlwind, tossed the file across the counter and said I should read what was inside right away.

"It turns out Uncle Wilbur was a Baptist minister out in Michigan," Polly said, "and his family wanted him buried back East, here in his hometown. But, according to Henry, the cause of the problem was that poor Reverend Wilbur was forced to wait in the post office, which had been a saloon and house of ill repute about 100 years ago. What with us being right out on the dock, the sailors would come into port after being out at sea for months at a time and head straight for that door—our entryway. This building was just a few steps off the gangplank. And it offered gambling and whiskey and wild women and anything else they wanted to buy. So . . . "

"So," I added, "the poor reverend was trapped in this wild whorehouse and was probably being attacked by the ghosts of the former gamblers and sinners. He was trying to get away from the evil temptations."

"Or," Polly said, "maybe he was being enticed and was trying to get out of that urn and have some fun, kick up his heels. After all, if he knew where he was going to be for eternity already, maybe he wanted to have a good time and needed somebody to release him from the tin can. But, instead," Polly said, shaking her head, "me and Henry, with the kindest of intentions, took him out of the best place he was ever able to be, in his real life or in his afterlife. And, instead, we tossed him up on the hill where there's no excitement happening and probably never will be."

"Well," I said, "some folks would say he's better off."

"Do you really think so?" Polly inquired, and I could see the beginning of a smile forming at the corners of her mouth.

"No, not really," I said.

"Neither do I," she said. "Neither do I."

Short Sightings

The following reports do not offer enough material for a separate chapter, but are interesting and worth sharing.

Drummer boy

Fort Delaware, Pea Patch Island

During a program in Old New Castle, a woman spoke to me before I began my presentation. She knew I conducted ghost tours at Fort Delaware and she told me of an incident that had occurred to her more than 30 years before.

"I was in my 20s," she said, "and had spent the day at the fort. It was a lot different than it is now. You could roam in places that I swear nobody had been since the Civil War. We had a great time. Then, that night, when I went to sleep I saw a Confederate ghost in my bedroom."

The lady said in the early morning, several hours after she had gone to sleep, the room became very cold and she decided to get up to determine the cause.

"I wanted to see if there was a window open," she said, "but I never got out of bed. I began to turn my body to put my feet on the floor and there, right at the side of my bed, was a Confederate drummer boy. He had to be about 15 or younger. He was standing there, with his drum at his side. I can still see his gray uniform perfect as day. Then, before I could scream or react, he began to drum and disappeared."

I wondered what she did.

"I didn't move," the lady said. "I pulled the covers up to my neck and suddenly, the room was warm again. Like it should have been. I never saw him again and I will never forget it. Ever."

I suggested that the sighting was a dream, that it was a suggestion in her mind because of her recent trip to the Pea Patch Island fort.

"I have heard those explanations and more for years," she said, waving a hand to tell me she didn't want to hear any more comments that might suggest the event hadn't happened.

"I was there. It was real. That's it!" she said. "And he has not been seen since, and I live in the same house. So I guess he was just passing through on his way back to Richmond."

When I asked her if she had been back to Fort Delaware, for the ghost tours or any other reason since then, she laughed, shook her head and replied, "Are you kidding?"

Activity in the barrack

Fort Delaware, Pea Patch Island

On Aug. 18, 2001, a new prisoner structure was dedicated at Fort Delaware State Park. This replica of a regulation wooden prison barrack, following original plans, was constructed in a clearing in front of the fort. The large building represents scores of similar prison barracks that covered about 15 acres of the island during the Civil War.

Each wooden structure held hundreds of Confederate prisoners. The first group to use the newly constructed building was a gathering of re-enactors who stayed overnight at the fort during its annual Garrison Weekend event.

The men, representing Confederate units, arrived on Pea Patch Island and stowed their belongings in the new building. That done, they left the site and roamed the island, renewing acquaintances with friends they had made over the years as they traveled to and spent weekends at various Civil War historic sites.

When they returned to bed down hours later, many of the weekend soldiers found that their equipment had been rummaged through and tossed around the large open building. But, the structure had been locked, and there was no logical explanation for what had occurred.

Throughout the rest of the weekend, several of the re-enactors who slept in the new building mentioned feeling uneasy, and a few said that some of their items had been moved and even lost. They reported tapping on the roof and the floor. One man claimed that a canteen floated across the room.

It's far too early to tell whether the new structure, built upon ground where the original prison buildings had stood 150 years earlier, is haunted. But the file has been opened, and if new unexplained reports come in, they will be added to the file on the "Prison Barrack on Pea Patch Island."

Along The Strand

New Castle, Delaware

Historic New Castle has a varied history that has included visits from famous pirates, wealthy merchants, Indians, sailors and soldiers, unknown slaves and some of the most famous officials in our country's early history.

Some believe the ghosts of certain former residents or those who passed through the town still remain—in spirit.

Along The Strand, a row of historic houses that have a wonderful view of the Delaware River, there is a report of an apparition of a young boy, in Colonial-era clothing who walks up the stairs. He appears during

Historic homes line Olde New Castle's streets, but who knows which ones host spirited guests.

both the day and evening, at irregular intervals. Apparently, in this home's case, he is seen only by the female owner of the residence.

"At first I was frightened, but after about a half-dozen sightings," she said, "it really didn't seem to bother me very much. After a while it was still interesting, but not horrifying. However, I soon realized that no one else who lived in the house could see him. After trying to convince my husband and daughter that the Little Fellow, that's what I call him, was floating around, and they thought I was crazy, I just gave up on them. Essentially, I decided to keep any reports of the boy's presence and activities to myself."

That was fine, she said, until the night before she was entertaining a group of lady friends for a night of bridge.

"I began to worry that one of my guests might see him," she told me, "then what would I do? I was terrified when they came, but things were out of my control."

To the host's satisfaction and surprise, the evening was an absolutely wonderful success.

"It was amazing," she said, smiling. "In the middle of one hand, two of the ladies began to complain about the cold temperature of the room. I was very comfortable and couldn't understand what they were talking about. After checking the heat and hearing their complaints for a third time, I looked up and my 'Little Fellow' was standing there, between my two lady friends. He was looking at their cards. I was shocked, but soon realized that no one knew he was there."

The young ghost seemed to be interested in the game, but had no knowledge of what the women were doing.

"He stood there among us for at least a half hour," the hostess said. "Then he went away and I had to turn down the heat. But, I have a plan for the next time my bridge group visits."

What's that? I wondered.

"I'm going to leave out this book on bridge rules and hope my ghostly friend reads up on the game. Then," she said, smiling, "he might be able to give me some hints about what they're holding and help me win the evening's prize."

Haunted lightship?

East Coast, U.S.A.

Along a narrow waterway–just outside the central business district of a small seaport–an old, rusted lightship stands. A narrow set of wooden stairs leads to the deck of this grounded, aging and forgotten relic that once served as a safety signal to mariners approaching the busy port.

Today the red-and-white rust bucket is under constant repair by a handful of volunteers who hope to improve its appearance and convert it into an educational tool that will explain the important role it played in maritime history. On weekends, a handful of workers try to hold back the effects of the elements and, at the same time, make some progress toward what seems to be a never-ending restoration project.

Ted, who performs volunteer maintenance on the craft, said he had the bad luck to experience an unexplained occurrence one weekend that continues to bother him many years later.

"We don't allow groups to go through the ship, and we also don't get many individuals who even ask to visit," he explained.

"And that's fine with us. You see, it's still in pretty bad shape, and we really can't afford for anyone to come in here and get hurt or fall. So we lock up the wire-mesh gate leading to the deck, even when we're inside working. What I'm saying is, if you're in here, you know exactly how many workers are with you and who they are. There's no way in or out without all of us knowing it."

One Sunday, late in the afternoon when Ted was alone, he heard heavy footsteps coming from the deck above. He said it startled him, because it was getting late, the sun was going down, and there was no one else but him working on the ship.

"I jumped three feet, I swear," he said. "I was down two decks, so it was right above me. It couldn't have been a kid throwing a rock or something on the main deck. That happens a lot. No. This was right above the area where I was working, on top of my head.

"I hoped it wouldn't happen again, but the moment I thought that to myself, damn if there weren't more footsteps, like somebody stamping their feet or boots, real hard."

Grabbing a long wrench, Ted ran to the next level, looked around and found there was nothing. He said he was standing at the spot where he figured the sounds had originated.

"Then, I heard more stamping again, the same kind, but this time above me, on the main deck. I dashed for the ladder, got on top and, again, nothing. At this point," Ted said, "I was scared. The sun was just about down. The wind began blowing. I was standing alone on this lightship deck that was rusted and eerie and there's no one there except me. Actually, I was glad there was no one there.

"I could see my car in the parking lot. There was no other sign of life, no cars, no kids, no people. I was visibly shaken. My hands were starting to tremble. How I wanted to be driving away just then. I had left my coat, with my car keys in the pocket, two decks below. So I had to go back down and get my stuff. All I had was a wrench and flashlight for protection. That was a very bad night."

Ted went downstairs. He said it took all the courage he could muster to make his legs move in front of each other.

"I remember listening for the slightest sound," he said, "but praying that I wouldn't hear anything. Do you understand? You want to be aware of everything, in case something happens so you're prepared to respond. But, at the same time, you don't want to know if something is there. You'll really be happy if whatever it is will leave you alone so you can get out of there safely. You want to get away and let it be somebody else's problem when you're not there."

Ted rushed to the walkway, locked the gate behind him and ran down the steps, across the lot and jumped into his car. He slammed and locked the door, and said his hands were shaking so much it took him several long seconds to get the key in the ignition slot.

"I never went back there alone to work," he said. "I don't even like riding by at night anymore. I'll go two blocks out of my way, just so I won't have to pass by that old boat. And, the funny thing is, I used to love to be in there working, but no more. It will never be the same."

I asked Ted if he had an explanation for the sounds.

"Those ships were out there in the bay, and crews were stuck on them for months at a time. God only knows what happened out there. Men died on those ships. Some deaths were accidental, like things that occur in storms. Some were from natural causes and old age. But I have to believe that some were probably from guys getting on each other's nerves and some deck hand being murdered or killed in a fight.

"I don't know if that happened on this particular lightship. I'll never know. No one will. Certain events that took place were never talked about. Those lightship sailors were a tough bunch, a special breed. They followed a code of silence, and what happened while at sea never left the sea, was buried at sea along with the bodies. It was never mentioned when they got back to port.

"I just have a feeling, based on the chills and sensations I felt that day when I heard those sounds, that what's on that ship—the ghost or spirit of the dead or whatever you want to call it—is not friendly. And whenever I go back there to work, which isn't nearly as often as it used to be, I never, ever go alone–and I only work there during the mornings, now."

Spooky fishing boat

Eastern Shore of Maryland

Ben owns a saloon on a side street in a small fishing town. It's located in one of those villages that used to be a working port. Now the old-fashioned storefronts are gone, and the streets are lined with antique malls, specialty boutiques, art shops, T-shirt stores and classy restaurants that serve wine with lunch and list strange menu items that the waiter has to explain.

In these transformed tourist towns, the real fishermen and old-timers exist in a small, hole-in-the-wall section that tourists never visit. And the locals like it that way.

Ben's Saloon is just such a place. It serves domestic beer, whiskey by the shot and large, fried sandwiches. It also offers comfortable, worn seats for the regulars to use as they share plenty of tall tales and locally oriented conversation.

One of the most often told stories in Ben's is about a haunted fishing boat.

As the tale goes, Ben's grandmother, Mary Alice, was being courted by two fishermen—Nevitte and Logan Alley John. She liked them both, but the time was approaching when she would have to make a choice.

"Grandma Mary Alice was approaching the ripe old age of 20," Ben, a big man with large arms, gray hair and an infectious smile, said. "So time was moving fast. She told the two men that after they returned from their next fishing trip she would have an answer. One would be her groom and the other would have to look elsewhere for a warm bed and good cooking."

That was in early winter, Ben explained, and no one knew for sure when the workboat would be back. It could be two days, could be a week. It depended on the weather and the size of the catch and a half-dozen other conditions over which the two-man crew had no control.

"Well, 10 days later," Ben said, "the *Free Spirit* pulled back into port, with only one of the two fishermen on board. Grandpa Nevitte, who I am told I favor, hit the dock, ran to my Grandma's place and told her that Logan Alley John was not going to come calling. He had fallen overboard during an accident and had been lost in the bay."

There was a funeral service the following Saturday for Logan Alley John, and a wedding of Nevitte and Mary Alice was held on Sunday–two festivities in two days. Village life returned to normal by Monday. From that day on, while Grandpa Nevitte was back in the Bay, his new bride was tending house. And she would take care of things at home for the two of them and their children during the next 35 years that they remained married.

"But," Ben said, "the strange thing is that my grandfather sold his boat after only two more trips in the Bay, and he became a storekeeper, even though they say he loved the water. He would never go back out to sea, not even to fish for pleasure. His former boat, on its first trip out with its new owner, caught fire and sank. Everyone aboard died at sea. Their bodies were never found. The boat was lost, disappeared.

"But it's been seen floating in area waterways for years. An odd coincidence is that there have been reports that a man wearing a long black beard pilots the ghostly craft. Interesting to most folks, including me, is that Logan Alley John wore a long black beard and died while working on that same boat."

I waited as Ben the saloonkeeper poured himself another drink.

"The real story is," he said, "the version my grandmother told me one day, when I was raving about how wonderful my grandfather was. She had to be about 80 at the time, an older lady but full of spunk. A fisherman's wife lives through a lot. She looked at me," Ben said, "and touched my face, then whispered, 'You're so much like your grandfather, full of fire and wild plans and you never wait, you're so impatient, just like him. You have to have everything right away.' "

When asked to explain, Ben said, "My grandmother told me she knew she had to choose between the two men, or they would drive her crazy or kill each other to prove which was a better fisherman. So she told them they would know after that last trip they took together. She admitted to me that she loved my grandfather more than Logan Alley John, but she never told him that. In fact, she used to tell my grandfather that she wanted him to be more like the other man, more like John. And that just got Grandpa Nevitte madder than hell.

"Anyway, on that last trip, when they were out in the Bay, just the two of them, there was a storm. My Grandma told me that my Grandpa was so worried he was going to get turned down, to lose her hand, that he killed Logan Alley John. Hit him over the head with a club and shoved his body into the rough water. That was the end of it. Problem solved. No more worries for anybody."

How did your grandmother find out, I wondered.

"She told me she knew," Ben said, "the moment my Grandpa sold his boat. He had loved that boat so much, she knew something

If old neglected boats could speak, oh what eerie tales they would tell.

was wrong. When reports came in later, of the ghost of Logan Alley John at the wheel of the *Free Spirit*, Grandpa Nevitte admitted everything to her."

But, the grandson said, his grandmother wasn't surprised or upset. "She told me, 'I knew he had something to do with John not coming back. That was just his way with things like that. I wasn't surprised. When they saw the ghost boat, he told me the whole story the very next day. Your grandfather knew I would figure it out. He was a smart man. Resourceful and smart. He also knew I was a clever woman.'

"I asked her," Ben recalled, "if she was troubled or bothered by the confession. Do you know what she told me? With a smile on her chapped and wrinkled lips, my Grandma looked at me, sort of surprised, and said, 'Upset? Oh, dear, of course not! I never planned to marry Logan Alley John in the first place. I just said all those crazy things to get Nevitte jealous. My Lord. And the nice thing about what your grandfather did, was I didn't have to hurt poor John's feelings. Things seemed to turn out very fine. Very fine indeed.' "

Ed and Kathleen Okonowicz

E d Okonowicz, a Delaware native, is an editor and writer at the University of Delaware, where he also teaches both storytelling and feature writing classes. Kathleen Burgoon Okonowicz, a watercolor artist and illustrator, is originally from Greenbelt, Maryland, and is an artist member of the Baltimore Watercolor Society.

Photo by Bob Cohen

A professional storyteller, Ed presents programs throughout the Mid-Atlantic region. He is a member of the Delaware Humanities Forum Speakers Bureau and Visiting Scholars Program and has served on the Maryland State Arts Council Traditional/Folk Arts Advisory Panel.

Kathleen enjoys taking things of the past and preserving them in her paintings. Her print, *Special Places*, features the stately stairway in Wilmington, Delaware, that was the "special place" of the characters in Ed's love story, *Stairway over the Brandywine*. In the fall of 1999, she released *Station No. 5,* a print that captures the charm of a 1893 Victorian-style firehouse also in Wilmington, near Trolley Square.

A graduate of Salisbury State University, Kathleen earned her master's degree in professional writing from Towson State University. In addition to painting, she teaches a self-publishing course at the University of Delaware.

As the owners of Myst and Lace Publishers Inc., Kathleen is responsible for art, photography, layout and design, while Ed conducts the interviews and writes the stories.

For information on storytelling, call Ed. For self-publishing or graphic design assistance, call Kathleen.
Telephone: 410 398-5013.

Also visit our web site at:
www.mystandlace.com

True
Ghost Stories
from Master Storyteller
Ed Okonowicz

Spirits
Between the Bays
Series

Volume by volume our haunted house grows.
Enter at your own risk!

Wander through the rooms, hallways and dark corners of this eerie series.

Creep deeper and deeper into terror, and learn about the area's history in our series of ghostly tales and folklore of the Mid-Atlantic region.

"If this collection doesn't give you a chill, check your pulse, you might be dead."

–Leslie R. McNair
The Review, University of Delaware

"This expert storyteller can even make a vanishing hitchhiker story fresh and startling."

–Chris Woodyard
author of *Haunted Ohio* series

POSSESSED OBJECTS PLAGUE THEIR OWNERS

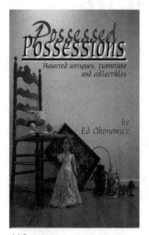

112 pages
5 1/2" x 8 1/2"
softcover
ISBN 0-9643244-5-8

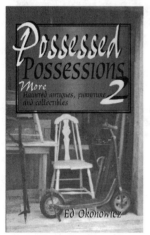

112 pages
5 1/2" x 8 1/2"
softcover
ISBN 0-890690-02-3

$9.95 each

A BUMP. A THUD. MYSTERIOUS MOVEMENT. Unexplained happenings. Caused by What? Venture through this collection of short stories and discover the answer. Experience 20 eerie, true tales about items from across the country that, apparently, have taken on an independent spirit of their own—for they refuse to give up the ghost.

From Maine to Florida, from Pennsylvania to Wisconsin . . haunted heirlooms exist among us . . . everywhere.

Read about them in *Possessed Possessions* and *Possessed Possessions* **2** the books some antique dealers **definitely** do not want you to buy.

"If you're looking for an unusual gift for a collector of antiques, or enjoy haunting tales, this one's for you."

—Collector Editions

"This book is certainly entertaining, and it's even a bit disturbing."

—Antique Week

". . . an intriguing read."

—Maine Antique Digest

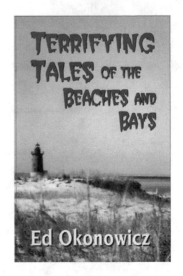

The DelMarVa Murder Mystery series

FIRED!

Early in the 21st century, DelMarVa, the newest state in the union, which includes Delaware and the Eastern Shore of Maryland and Virginia, is plagued by a ruthless serial killer. In FIRED! meet Gov. Henry McDevitt, Police Commissioner Michael Pentak and State Psychologist Stephanie Litera as they track down the peninsula's worst killer since 19th century murderess Patty Cannon.

Ed Okonowicz

320 pages
4 1/4" x 6 3/4"
softcover
ISBN 1-890690-01-5
$9.95

WELCOME to the State of DelMarVa

"Politics and romance make fairly strange bedfellows, but add a dash of mystery and mahem and the result can be spectacular, as evidenced in FIRED!"
—Sharon Galligar Chance
BookBrowser Review

"Lots of familiar places in this imaginative suspense novel."
—Jeannine Lahey
About.com
Wilmington, Del.

". . . this is Okonowicz's best book so far!"
—The Star Democrat
Easton, Md.

Halloween House

In *Halloween House*, the series continues as Gov. McDevitt, Commissioner Pentak and other DelMarVa crime fighters go up against Craig Dire, a demented businessman who turns his annual Halloween show into a real-life chamber of horrors.

320 pages
4 1/4" x 6 3/4"
softcover
ISBN 1-890690-03-1
$9.95

Delaware Press Association First Place Award 2000

"Halloween House mystery chills summer heat."
—Rosanne Pack
Cape Gazette

"Looking at the front cover, the reader knows it's going to be a bumpy night."
—Erika Quesenbery
The Herald

www.mystandlace.com

Disappearing Delmarva
Portraits of the Peninsula People

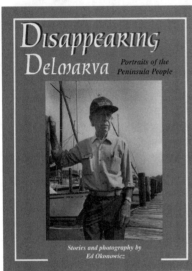

Disappearing Delmarva
Portraits of the Peninsula People

Stories and photography by
Ed Okonowicz

208 pages
8 1/2" x 11"
Hardcover
ISBN 1-890690-00-7

$38.00

Photography and stories
by Ed Okonowicz

Disappearing Delmarva introduces you to more than 70 people on the peninsula whose professions are endangered. Their work, words and wisdom are captured in the 208 pages of this hardbound volume, which features more than 60 photographs.

Along the back roads and back creeks of Delaware, Maryland, and Virginia—in such hamlets as Felton and Blackbird in Delaware, Taylors Island and North East in Maryland, and Chincoteague and Sanford in Virginia—these colorful residents still work at the trades that have been passed down to them by grandparents and elders.

Winner of 2 First-Place Awards:

Best general book
Best Photojournalism entry

National Federation of Press Women Inc.
1998 Communication Contest

Ed presents a program based on this award-winning book at local historical societies and libraries. Contact him at 410 398-5013 to arrange a program in your area.